SOME THINGS WORTH KNOWING

A Generalist's Guide to Useful Knowledge

SOME THINGS WORTH KNOWING

A GENERALIST'S GUIDE TO USEFUL KNOWLEDGE

by

Stuart Chase

HARPER & BROTHERS, PUBLISHERS, NEW YORK

CONTENTS

It is absolutely impossible to approach the urgent and distressful problems of the present time with any hope of lucid solution until a general background of knowledge is definitely present in the mind.

— H. G. WELLS

Concern for man himself and his fate must always form the chief interest of all technical endeavors. . . . Never forget this in the midst of your diagrams and equations.

— ALBERT EINSTEIN

FOREWORD

THIS BOOK is an experiment, possibly a foolhardy one. It is an attempt to distinguish useful and usable knowledge from the vast ocean of facts in the encyclopedias. What should the intelligent layman have ready to mind in the age of the atom?

To cope with the tough problems ahead of us we should be able to see all the way around them. Experts and specialists are invaluable, but, as specialists, they see only the trees, sometimes only the twigs under the trees. We need power to see the woods. We need generalists who do not get lost in the trees. This does not mean two kinds of people, for everyone is a specialist in some degree, perhaps as a typist, perhaps as a nuclear physicist. It means more room in our minds for the over-all view, especially for relationships and balancing of alternatives.

I am breaking a few rules, for authors are not supposed to write about a subject unless they are specialists in it. Still less are they supposed to write about as many subjects as are considered in this book. (Not *covered*, in some cases only touched on.) One reason for breaking rules is my conviction that they have been overdone; they have become too rigid. The competence of the specialist today has overawed the intelligent layman until he says: "It's way over my head; I'll leave it to the experts." How often do we all say or think something like that? Yet it is a dangerous attitude in this day and age. It tends to create an oligarchy of knowledge, which can become a monopoly of power, a series of tight little principalities with no minds left to survey the whole country.

I know a generalist who is also a learned specialist. He has written me that he would like to tell his specialist confreres: "Wake up! Live at the level of your time! Crawl out of that talent-trap which you refer to as your 'field' and look around. You may learn something about the only era you will ever live in, and about the only species you will ever be a member of. You will certainly learn something about yourself!"

To leave learning exclusively to specialists is not only dangerous but weak. It deprives civilized people of an essential part of their life on earth, something that many primitive peoples have naturally exercised—the full expression of curiosity, honestly confronting the mystery of existence, trying to understand their world and themselves. It is pitiful to retreat from this facing of life, especially at a time when so much new knowledge is coming in. Even if the astrophysicists have shown the universe to be far grander and more complex than we used to think, shall we say: "It's all beyond me," and turn our backs and go indoors? Or shall we look up with new wonder and delight, trying to imagine the vast recesses of the whirling sky? Similarly for the marvels unfolding before the electronic microscope, and for new aspects of human behavior now being revealed.

Needless to say, my selection of areas of useful knowledge is a highly personal one. Another author would make a different and perhaps more adequate selection, mapping the woods with greater precision. But both of us would unite in opposing an invasion by specialists waving monographs and differential equations. We are interested here not in technical detail, but in knowledge which should be common coin for intelligent laymen everywhere, subject to common discussion, and furnishing a basis for common action. As the sciences advance on the exponential curve they are riding, certain conclusions herein will of course be revised. Today, for instance, we do not know how the first particle of living matter was formed; tomorrow we may. Tomorrow we shall certainly know more about the structure of the atom as cyclotrons grow ever more powerful.

Homo sapiens is a single species, and his most serious problems—nuclear war, fall-out, population pressure, wastes of irreplaceable resources—affect the whole species. Technical experts, as we know, are making the planet smaller day by day, till we are in danger, as James Thurber says, of crashing into ourselves from behind. This book is written by an American, necessarily influenced by his culture and language, and will be read, if at all, mostly by Americans. Nevertheless it is addressed to generalists of every culture, East and West. I have tried to keep constantly in mind a thoughtful citizen of Japan, India, Egypt, Denmark, Brazil, Russia.

Up to a point some six thousand years ago, this universal view is easy to maintain, for cities, kingdoms, empires, armies, religions, civilizations were still to come. Curiosity, embryo science and art were there, but not the pyramids of the Nile nor those of Teotihuacán. Generalists the world around can look back on early man with a brotherly eye— our common ancestor, tough, adaptable and intelligent.

This study does not pretend to be either original research or an intensive combing of the documents. My sources are four: (1) data in easy reach of memory; (2) data gathered in my earlier books and articles which stand up as useful knowledge; (3) some recent reports, dependable but not too technical, on astrophysics, archaeology, etc.; and (4) a few recent summaries, again not too technical, such as *Frontiers of Knowledge* and *The Scientific American Reader*, to refresh my memory and add up-to-date material.

The reader will find a good deal of discussion and comparison concerning Russia and the United States, the two greatest power centers in the world at the moment. Their cultures, ideologies, economic and political systems are reviewed at some length. This attention is aimed not at solving the power struggle between them, but at employing this highly dynamic current situation as a laboratory in which to focus various beams of knowledge to see if they are useful.

I want to thank Fred Hoyle for scanning the early chapters, William Karraker for reviewing the first draft of the entire manuscript in the role of intelligent layman. My thanks go out to Evan Thomas for many helpful suggestions, to Christine Loring and Lola Donnell for efficient secretarial help, and to my dear wife for devoted and unlimited editorial work, for drafting parts of several chapters, and for compiling the reading list.

STUART CHASE

Redding, Connecticut
August, 1958

1. The Quiz Program and the Generalist

I HAVE a grandson named Alan, who learns fast and asks a lot of questions. If he is really interested in the subject you do not have to tell the answer twice. He has tied it to previous experience and stored it away in that remarkable filing cabinet, the human brain, ready to come out later. Sometimes it comes out so accurately that it surprises me. I answer his question if I can; if not I show him how to look it up, thus instructing both of us.

I keep wondering how Alan, and all the other keen boys and girls I see coming out of the school and getting into yellow buses, are going to deal with the grave questions which are looming over the horizon in a tomorrow of unlimited power and unlimited possibilities of catastrophe. H. G. Wells used to talk about a race between education and catastrophe, and the observation is more true now than when he first made it, at the time of World War I. Are those youngsters learning what they need to know in that school?

FIFTY QUESTIONS

Dr. George Gallup once put fifty questions to eleven hundred students in twelve American and British universities.[1] He called the quiz a kind of "cultural Olympics," covering history, literature, religion, art, philosophy, archi-

---

[1] *Look*, May 29, 1956.

tecture, science, economics, music and language. The questions ran along like this:

> Who wrote *The Divine Comedy*?
> What is the dominant religion of Pakistan?
> Name one philosopher before Plato.
> What was the "Malthusian doctrine"?
> Who was Pavlov?
> What is a gene?
> When did China become a republic?

Oxford students came out on top, with an average of 35 questions correctly answered. Yale scored 26, the University of Georgia 21. After scoring myself and my wife—we both bettered Oxford—we began to think seriously about this cultural Olympic. The questions were fair enough, but how many of them tapped really vital knowledge? How many should an intelligent American or Englishman keep on the top of his mind? How many should an intelligent East Indian or Chinese gentleman have at his command? I made a rough division, and concluded that an intelligent layman, anywhere on the planet, not specializing in one of these subjects, might well have the answers readily available to twenty-three of the fifty, such as:

> What is the second law of thermodynamics?
> Name a book by Karl Marx.
> What is meant by *laissez faire*?
> Who is the father of psychoanalysis?
> Name three religions besides Christianity.

He should know how to look up the other twenty-seven questions if the discussion or the headlines swung in that direction, questions such as:

> What is a flying buttress?
> Who said, "I think, therefore I am"?
> What is La Scala?
> Who wrote "Finlandia"?

The reader may not agree in detail with my selections. But I think he will agree with the principle involved, namely, that some knowledge should be in every intelligent person's head ready for use on common problems; much knowledge can be left to specialists and the reference books.

QUIZ PROGRAM

M.C. on Studio 21: "Are you ready for the question?"

Van Looman: (Forcing smile) "What is life itself but a question?"

M.C.: "Very well. What year was the world's largest stream salmon taken in this country, where, and by whom? What length fly rod? What size hook and type of fly? What was the weight of the fish and the number of salmon eggs found inside?"

The above satire from the *TV Guide* strikes, I think, the authentic quiz-program note. These programs today seem to be building to a climax where a vast audience breathlessly awaits the first bookkeeper or stonemason or eleven-year-old to hit a jackpot of one million dollars. I saw Charles Van Doren go down to defeat in the spring of 1957, and I have collected a sample of the questions addressed to him and to the other virtuosos in the same season.

Who were the wives of Ulysses, Jason, Agamemnon, and Hector?

What animal provides mohair?

Name five breeds of non-sporting dogs.

Who are the kings of Denmark, Norway, Sweden, Belgium, Jordan and Iraq?

Standing on his accumulated $143,000, Mr. Van Doren, after naming all the other kings correctly in the last question, said "Leopold" for Belgium, adding with agony on his face, "I know it's wrong." So he skidded $14,000 down to $129,000—less tax—and lost his crown.

Mr. Teddy Nadler, a clerk in an Army depot, went to grammar school for six years, then took a job. Later in a settlement house he stumbled on a reference library and

apparently swallowed it whole. He built up a TV estate
even vaster than Van Doren's, and gave a reporter the
secret of his success. "My God, I can remember things like
when Pyrrhus landed in 280 B.C., he had twenty thousand
foot soldiers, two thousand archers, three thousand horse
soldiers and five hundred slingers." Mr. Nadler then named
all the major islands of the Philippine archipelago, together
with their areas. "I've always been wonderful on islands,"
he admitted.

Mr. Nadler is also wonderful on boxing statistics, movies,
classical music, baseball and European history. The only
item which gave him serious pause over a thirty-eight-week
period was naming five full generals in the Confederate
Army. He missed Samuel Cooper and Braxton Bragg.

On the American TV screen today you may also see
youngsters of Alan's age who possess an encyclopedic
knowledge of electronics, astronomy, or the stock market.
They can give you broker's nicknames for Texas Gulf
Sulphur or Reed Roller Bit, on the nail. They can give you
the three corporations with the largest defense contracts in
1956, or the three which paid dividends in the stock of other
companies. Is this useful knowledge for all of us, or merely
entertainment?

A friend tells me that his typist can do no work in the
morning until she has given him a play-by-play account of
last night's quiz show. She speaks, he is sure, for fifty
million devoted fans. Her story falls into three parts: (1)
How the contestants looked, especially the one she is back-
ing: "His face was all screwed up when he came out of
the booth." (2) How fairly one candidate or another was
treated by the M.C.: "She only answered half of it but he
gave her credit for all of it, and that's not right!" (3) How
much money changed hands: "He's up to ninety-six thousand dollars, but this salesman got three thousand dollars
even though he missed. He took it instead of a Cadillac."
At this point my friend inquires what the questions were,

and normally draws a blank. "Oh, something about baseball, or was it rivers? I can't remember—but you should have seen his face when he came out of that booth."

The formula is simple. Provide a contest in which the viewer can become emotionally involved with one or another of the contestants; provide a whacking great pot of gold, which shifts up and down by easily calculated rules. Then any old question will do. This, at least, is my friend's conclusion.

We can be sure, I think, that most quiz questions are not contributions to useful knowledge. Did you ever hear one begin with the word "Why"? There is little in them that anyone needs to know, unless he specializes in the subject. Charles Van Doren, an honest young scholar, admitted the point when he said that "quiz programs are not the way to disseminate knowledge." Mr. Nadler, when $120,000 ahead of the game, was even franker: "I'm a nitwit except for my memory," he said, and proceeded to regurgitate an entire scene from *Julius Caesar*.

TOTAL RECALL

Some psychologists believe that everything we hear, read or experience is stored away in the brain by a memory mechanism as yet imperfectly understood. Other students believe that much is lost; but all agree on the vastness of the filing system. "In the darkness of a little bone box, scarcely eight inches in length, an ordinary man or woman will store ten times more information than there is on all the shelves of a large library." [2]

Most of us, however, no matter how extensive our schooling, cannot consciously extract more than a small portion of this information—the visible iceberg above the water. In dreams, in psychoanalysis, hypnosis, somewhat more may be revealed. Miss Hawkes recalls the case of a maidservant of a professor who recited long passages of Hebrew which

---

[2] Jacquetta Hawkes, anthropologist, in *New York Times Magazine*, July 7, 1957.

she had heard, only once, from the lips of her employer. Half-awake, I sometimes hear many bars of a Mozart symphony with full orchestration, though I could not construct one note upon another while fully conscious.

A few individuals like Van Doren and Nadler, at the far end of the frequency distribution curve, can dredge up from memory practically the whole iceberg. They are born with what scientists term "total recall," something which no memory system can ever teach. This extraordinary faculty, be it noted, was of little use to Mr. Nadler, a clerk at sixty-nine dollars a week, before TV came along.

As to moppets whose brain boxes are stuffed with stock-market statistics and batting averages, Dr. Norbert Wiener of the Massachusetts Institute of Technology, the inventor of cybernetics, and once an infant prodigy himself, offers a somber comment. A prodigy, he says, may have an under-water memory or be quick to learn from books, but he has had little contact with life. Despite his total recall he is still a child, with a child's limited experience. Dr. Wiener pleads that such children be not "thrown to the lions of popular entertainment. They may have something important to give to the world which they cannot give if their values are early warped by inflated gifts of money and the rigors of the showman's bench."

KNOWLEDGE, USEFUL AND OTHERWISE

All of which brings us squarely to our own large question: What is useful knowledge for this day and age? What should an intelligent citizen have in clear view above the water line? It may be presumptuous to seek an answer, but there the question is, and there it promises to remain for a long time to come.

One should not call the answers to most quiz questions "useless knowledge." Far from it. For some students in some circumstances the answer may be vital, quite apart from passing examinations, or accumulating another eleven thousand dollars on Twenty One. A better distinction is between *general* and *specialized* knowledge. The former is what we

should know in our day-by-day living for intelligent judgments and decisions; the latter is what some of us need to
know for our livelihood, or our hobbies and pleasure. It is
like the distinction between "liberal arts" and vocational or
professional education, except that the liberal arts, as often
defined, include much that is irrelevant if not useless.

Applying the distinction to the person I know best, namely
myself, I have a fair amount of specialized knowledge concerning economics, accounting, semantics, and can lose the
intelligent layman rapidly, if I care to, in these subjects. The
layman, if he specializes in astrophysics, or the history of the
Third Republic, can lose me with equal rapidity. But both
of us should possess a body of vital general knowledge where
neither becomes lost. That is what we are looking for in this
book.

ANTI-KNOWLEDGE

There is a third category, namely, things not proved and
probably untrue. It represents a very considerable accumulation in civilized societies and undoubtedly an even larger
one among nature peoples. Here are the encrusted superstitions, the black cats, the old wives' tales, the little green
men who jump out of grounded flying saucers—all the un-
verified lore which stands in contradiction to the findings
of competent observers. The human mind, like nature, seems
to abhor a vacuum. If no dependable explanation is available, we seek a poetic or magical one. Our modern superstitions and much of our folklore are a cultural lag, coming
down from prescientific ages when natural phenomena remained unexplained. The vacuum was filled and the mind
eased, not with knowledge but with anti-knowledge. Bleed-
ing the patient, a widely accredited therapy in George
Washington's time, is anti-knowledge today.

Until the age of science was well established, knowledge
was sought by astrologers and alchemists to three chief ends:

1. To find the "philosopher's stone" which would trans-
mute base metals into gold.

2. To brew the elixir of life, which would permit one to live for two or three hundred years.

3. To foretell the future, the precise date of the end of the world, and propitious moments for getting married, undertaking a journey, or commencing any enterprise from "setting up a cobbler's shop to the marching of an army." [3]

Interestingly enough, the alchemist Gerber, while experimenting for the philosopher's stone, discovered corrosive sublimate, red oxide of mercury, nitric acid and nitrate of silver—knowledge of great use to specialists.

Astrology was popular with most of the crowned heads—as later it was said to be popular with Adolf Hitler. Kepler, the great astronomer, was forced to cast nativities (horoscopes) for a fee to keep from starving, though he knew it was nonsense. Scientific astronomy at the time was not a paying career.

If one desired to live for three hundred years, many learned formulas were at hand, among them this one: "Every night upon going to bed, he must put upon his heart a plaster composed of oriental saffron, red rose-leaves, sandalwood, aloes and amber, liquified in oil of roses and the best white wax. . . ." Anti-knowledge of this variety persists today chiefly among those deprived of much education.

Perhaps the most virulent form of modern anti-knowledge is found in mass stereotypes about foreigners, strangers, "out-groups." Thus the French are notoriously immoral, the Scotch notoriously stingy, the Americans notoriously money-mad—that kind of thing. Russians, at least under Stalin, were crammed with anti-knowledge about America, while Americans cherished plenty of anti-knowledge about Russia.

ON BEING A GENERALIST

If an expert is somebody who knows more and more about less and less until he knows everything about nothing, and

---

[3] *Extraordinary Popular Delusions* (Charles Mackay, London, 1841; republished by Farrar, Straus & Cudahy, 1956). A veritable gold mine of anti-knowledge, and long a favorite of Bernard M. Baruch, who contributes a foreword.

the size of the area in which a person has competence must continually diminish, the logical end would be the collapse of society, where nobody is left with an over-all view.

A story that went the rounds of New York's Madison Avenue in 1958 gently mocked the extreme specialist. A copywriter being interviewed for a job in an advertising agency is asked if he has worked on cigarette accounts.

"Oh, yes."
"On king-size cigarettes?"
"Yes."
"King-size filters?"
"Yes."
"King-size cork-tip filters?"
"Yes."
"King-size cork-tip filters in a flip-top box?"
"Yes."
"Mentholated king-size cork-tip filters in a flip-top box?"
"No. Not mentholated."
"Sorry. We need an expert."

The only way to break this trend toward more and more about less and less is to give specialists enough general knowledge to keep in communication with one another, and to see where their society and their planet are headed. Every intelligent man and woman, for instance, ought to be aware of the world-wide danger of H-bomb fall-out to future generations. Only geneticists, however, are competent to spell out the technical aspects of the danger and the statistical probabilities involved.

Again, everyone should know something about the international agencies in which most civilized nations now cooperate—the United Nations, the World Court, the Postal Union, the weather services, the Red Cross. But only a few fans need to know who won the gold medal for throwing the javelin in the 1936 Olympic Games. Americans should always carry the Bill of Rights in the forefront of their minds, but the fine points of the trial of Alger Hiss can be left to legal specialists.

Forward-looking universities, says John W. Gardner, president of the Carnegie Corporation, want their professional students to have a solid base of general education—"specialists who are capable of functioning as generalists." The narrowly trained specialist, he says, may be in for a nasty jolt as his skills grow out of date. "The only safety for the years ahead lies in a professional training sufficiently broad and flexible so that the individual can survive the ups and downs and adapt himself to changing situations."

President William Stevenson of Oberlin also makes an eloquent plea for generalists: "We must admit quite frankly that we are not as interested in producing skilled people as we are in producing educated people, educated in the sense that they can relate experience and knowledge in one field to problems in others. . . ."

Gilbert W. Chapman, corporation president and friend of good books, says that the problems of an executive become less specialized and more general as he climbs the business ladder. "The specialist cannot function effectively at the top level of management if all he brings to it is his specialty." This agrees with the spreading movement to give top executives in U.S. corporations a sabbatical year in which to study the liberal arts.

A mature mind combines reliable information with good judgment, and one definition of good judgment is appreciation of relationships between fields of information. In considering a delinquent boy, for instance, a good judge inquires into his past experience—family background, schooling, street life; his physical constitution and medical history; his abilities for future development, and opportunities which may be available for a better education and a useful life.

It is not impossible that some elder of a Stone Age tribe, living ten thousand years ago in Iran or Mexico, had as good a mechanism for judgment as, say, Thomas Jefferson or Niels Bohr. But his information was woefully meager. The nature of his own body, of his community, of the earth and its creatures, of the seas, the solar system, the stars—much of this was pure vacuum. He filled it with imaginary entities.

Today many blank spaces have been filled in. If a person has, or acquires, good judgment, he can use it with assurance on a body of knowledge incomparably greater than that available to a Socrates of the Stone Age, or even to Socrates himself. People may have no better brains today, but they have far more dependable knowledge on which to exercise them.

We will now turn to the consideration of various areas of knowledge which would seem to be important to the generalist. He has much of this knowledge already stored in his memory, but may not be able readily to get it out. I have heard, or read, a large part of what we are about to consider, but I never organized it, never worked out many of the relationships, in truth never until now made a serious attempt to distinguish between different sorts of knowledge. I had a benevolent idea that all knowledge was valuable, not realizing that a tidal flood is growing which could overwhelm a Leonardo.

We will begin with the largest field of all, the universe. Others might prefer the smallest, the core of the atom; or the most familiar, say the food supply. To me, however, the universe is the place to start. What is known about it gives the background against which all else is staged.

2. The Generalist Views the Universe

AT ANY given moment the reader will be going in four directions at fantastic speeds without knowing it. He is turning with the earth's rotation at seven hundred miles an hour (in the Temperate Zone); he is being carried by the earth in its yearlong derby around the sun at seventy thousand miles an hour; he is swinging with the solar system around the track of the Milky Way at a million miles an hour; while the whole Milky Way galaxy—which is our home galaxy—is headed for an unlocated destination at a speed as yet uncalculated but superlatively high.

If the reader boards a train from Washington to St. Louis, he can add two more motions to the four above, making six altogether at a given instant. He can be walking back to the dining car at three miles an hour, while the train travels westward at seventy miles an hour. The walking he will be aware of, but on a smooth track he will hardly notice the motion of the train unless he looks out the window.

Every one of us is subject to these motions and they typify our umbilical ties to the universe. We live on the planet earth, which is part of the solar system, which is part of the Milky Way galaxy, which is only one of millions of galaxies in that portion of the universe that telescopes have so far revealed. They have revealed distances in excess of a billion light years.

The connections are reasonably clear and some of the speeds have been worked out. We do not know why we are here, or where we are going at these headlong speeds—and probably we never shall. But it seems a good idea to find out what we can of the rules; scientists have learned more about them in the last fifty years than in all previous astronomical history. In another half century their present findings will doubtless seem elementary,[1] but enough is at hand to be useful to the generalist as well as the specialist. We have acquired in effect a whole new set of models of reality since 1900, not only in astronomy but in almost every field of investigation. Sometimes the models support the wisdom of the ages, often they do not.

The new scientific findings give us the most probable shape of the cosmos and our whole environment, in the middle of the twentieth century A.D. The shape has changed drastically under the impact of Einstein's theory of relativity, of Max Planck's quantum theory, of the culture concept of the anthropologists—to name three outstanding new models. Neither the physical universe nor human societies look as they did to intelligent people in 1900. The new knowledge suggests, on the whole, a friendlier universe, with fewer malign forces against which we are helpless.

It is not always easy for the layman to follow the scientist as he blocks out his models. The English language, indeed most spoken languages, set up severe restrictions. In English one thinks of *time* as a linear flow going on and on—and where will it all end? Or we trace the flow back and back in our minds—and where did it all begin? One thinks of *space* going out to the horizon, up to the sky, and on and out to the uttermost galaxy—and what lies beyond that? In our experience, there has always been something on the other side of every door.

Scientists have liberated themselves from ordinary lan-

---

[1] Some scientists are beginning to speculate on the universe of anti-matter, not to be confused with anti-knowledge.

guage by developing the special language of mathematics.
They find the universe is not to be described in terms of
earthly doors, or a linear flow of time. Space, they say, is
curved, time is a fourth dimension, and "space-time" is the
expression which best covers the situation. At the speed of
light, 186,000 miles per second, they tell us time stands still.
Already they are blocking out experiments to test whether a
man on a space ship will age as rapidly as a man on the
ground.

We laymen, no matter how intelligent and learned, cannot understand this talk except in a very general way, and it
is foolish to try to force comprehension. What we can understand is that the astrophysicist perceives the cosmos in terms
of special languages. These bring him closer to reality than
we can come in English—or French or Chinese. We can also
understand that a Hopi Indian, thinking in the Hopi language—which does not treat time as a flow—has less trouble
with the fourth dimension than do we.[2] If we really wish to
see the universe as scientists see it, we know that we can do
it with the help of calculus and other special languages.

The generalist is quite willing to leave the detailed picture of the universe to the physicists, the astronomers and
the mathematicians. But there are things to be said about it
in plain English—or plain Russian or Arabic—which belong
in every intelligent layman's mental equipment, to help him
orient himself within the universe as a small but dynamic
part of it.

FOUR MODELS

It is fascinating to compare changing concepts about the
cosmos, from culture to culture, and over the centuries. Four
patterns are outstanding:

Model 1. Nature peoples saw the earth as a flat base on
which the universe rested. Above it spread the dome of the
sky, across which the sun, moon and stars passed in orderly

---

2 Following Benjamin Lee Whorf: *Language, Thought and Reality* (Massachusetts Institute of Technology Press, 1956).

procession, to return by some mysterious underground path. Early Chinese and Babylonian astronomers also assumed a flat earth, though they were more precise in their observations. Most primitive tribes today are flat-earth philosophers.

Model 2. The Greeks guessed that the earth was round. Was it because they could see the galley's mast after the hull had sunk below the horizon of the Aegean? They placed the earth at the center of a spherical universe, with the heavenly bodies circling deferentially around it. This pattern solved the underground-return problem. First Eudoxus, 400 B.C., then Ptolemy assumed the earth was fixed, while the sun, moon, planets and stars moved around the center in a structure like a dinner plate, their arcs perfect Euclidean circles. Five planets were identified by the Greeks, all lying on this dinner plate. It was—and still is for that matter— pleasanter to think of the earth as the hub of the universe, and man as the most important creation thereon. The Ptolemaic model gave the human ego a wonderful lift, and was abandoned only after a violent ideological struggle, which involved the death sentence for some courageous thinkers.

Model 3. The Polish astronomer Copernicus about the middle of the sixteenth century published a book demonstrating that the sun was really the center of the solar system, that the planets circled around the sun, with the fixed stars beyond. In one of the boldest steps ever taken in the history of ideas, he demolished the towering authority of Ptolemy, the Greek philosophers and the Church. Galileo invented the telescope, which supported Copernicus with visible evidence, and presently Newton expounded his majestic laws of gravitation to explain why the planets moved the way they did. Using Newton's laws, Adams and Leverrier calculated where another planet ought to be, and called it Neptune. Presently the telescope found it.

We look up at the sky on a clear, moonless night. Yes, in an hour's time, we can see that one bright star advances in relation to the others, which remain in fixed patterns, like the Great Dipper, as they move across the heavens. The bright star is one of the planets, shining by light reflected from the sun, not by its own atomic reaction. A student of the night sky without instruction might conclude that this bright body and a few others were unique in their movements. He might note, after years of observation, that they regularly appeared at certain seasons and moved in predictable paths.

But how in the name of reason and common sense did Copernicus and Kepler, without adequate instruments, accumulate the evidence to overturn the authority of the ages and give us a correct model of the solar system? Look again at the sky, and ask yourself how long it would take you, an intelligent layman, to duplicate their conclusion. Then stand in all humility before this soaring achievement of the human mind.

Model 4. After Newton, scientists thought the universe was charted for all time. The gravitational equations could explain everything—if one had the patience to work them through. (This was long before electronic computers.) When Einstein prepared a new model—or more accurately an improved model—scientists were deeply shocked. Some of them have not yet recovered. Einstein did not have to battle as fiercely as Copernicus, but he had to lay experiment after experiment on the line and predict the outcome, before his model was accepted.

At the moment, Einstein's model is the latest, but it would be rash to say that it is final. Each model, be it noted, gave a closer fit to reality than the one before, and Model 5, when it comes, will be closer still.[3] We need not include among our models the learned construct of John Cleves Symmes, who persuaded a good many people in the early 1900's, including several members of Congress, that the world was a hollow sphere habitable on the inside. A prime specimen of anti-knowledge.

---

[3] Heisenberg in Germany is working on a "unified field theory" which could become Model 5.

The generalist is aware that Einstein not only made a drastic improvement on the Newtonian universe, but created a kind of earthquake in human thinking. He forced scientists to abandon Absolutes, such as absolute time and absolute space, and think in terms of probabilities, processes and relationships. We will return to this revolution in a moment.

THEORIES ABOUT THE ORIGIN OF THE UNIVERSE

How did the universe begin? The idea of special creation has been discarded. Fred Hoyle, the brilliant Cambridge astronomer, speculates upon a steady discharge of "background material," mostly hydrogen atoms, into the universe from unknown sources.[4] "Continuous creation," he calls it. Some scientists subscribe to the "big bang" theory, which starts everything in a mighty explosion. Why, and out of what, is not elaborated.

Perhaps the most favored theory today, however, is the *dust-cloud hypothesis,* which accounts for many observed phenomena, if not for all. It begins with gigantic clouds of gas and dust composed of tiny particles of hydrogen, oxygen, nitrogen, carbon, surging around in space. How they got there is not stated. In due course, stars are formed from this cosmic dust, as the particles gather in clots and proceed to attract more particles by gravitation. First comes a whirling disc of dust, then condensations, thickenings, and finally a star—give or take a few billion years in the process. Stars in the same general area attract one another to form a galaxy, an elliptical structure revolving around a center. The Milky Way is such a galaxy, with our sun, a relatively undistinguished member, way out on its edge. There appear to be an astronomical number of galaxies beyond the Milky Way, formed by a similar process.

Inside a normal star, the swept-up hydrogen is constantly being converted into helium—an exercise in atomic fusion at a temperature of about ten million degrees. Gradually this inferno of conversion approaches the surface, and the

---

4 Perhaps from old exploded suns?

star becomes hotter. After a great burst of inconceivable heat, sometimes called a "nova," the star may subside into a "white dwarf," or a "black dwarf." In our own galaxy, says Hoyle, not only are new stars being formed, but each star is continually sweeping up stray clouds of interstellar gas and adding to its mass.

How old is the universe? How large is it? How empty? Where is it going, and how will it end? These questions we can leave to the specialists, perhaps asking them to make sure, following Bridgman's operational definition, that they are not meaningless questions. A meaningless question, says Bridgman, is one for whose answer no operation can be performed, one which lies beyond experimental proof.

Useful knowledge for the generalist to keep in mind is that the universe is on the move, dynamic, creating new suns and new planets as old stars burn out. It is composed of atoms, molecules, energies, radiations, similar to those we know on earth, on a scale incomparably grand. This universal energy, powering our sun, activates the forms that we call life. Even the materials we handle are part of a homogeneous whole. "The great majority of the atoms in the human body," says George W. Gray, "are hydrogen atoms. We are such stuff as stars are made of. The sense of kinship in life stuff with star stuff is inescapable. It touches astronomers, physicists, geochemists, as well as sentimental laymen." [5]

THE EINSTEIN REVOLUTION

As a young man I read Haeckel's *Riddle of the Universe*, a riddle which the author modestly admitted he had practically solved. The universe, as I understood him, was a rigid, uncompromising mechanism, composed of particles put in motion by gravitation, an explanation based on the Newtonian model.

Newton worked from Kepler's generalizations about planetary motion to find a broader generalization, and discovered

---

[5] *Harper's Magazine*, March, 1958.

it in the law of gravitation. Motion from one mass to another —whether an apple, an ocean liner or the sun—is the result of the gravitational force of mutual attraction. It is this force which keeps planets spinning, the moon in its orbit, tides surging, sputniks circling, and "holds the universe together." Each mass attracts every other inversely as the square of the distance between them—the nearer the stronger.

These laws seemed to describe the fundamental structure of the cosmos once and for all. They imposed a finality on research which greatly impeded the growth of physics. New ideas about energy, for instance, were ruled out. Laplace was ready to forecast the fate of the universe, given the position and speed of every atom. Says J. Bronowski in *The Common Sense of Science*, a lucid summary which we shall follow in the next few pages:

> Einstein found the flaw in Newton's theory by looking into its heart. There he found the assumption that *time* and *space* are given absolutely, and are alike for all observers. Einstein showed there is no universal "now," only a "here and now" for each observer, so that space and time are inextricably woven together, aspects of a single reality. Moreover the structure of space, in turn, cannot be disentangled from the matter which is embedded in it.

Between any event, whether an eclipse of the sun or the flight of a baseball, and the scientist who observes it, a signal must pass—a ray of light, a sound wave, an impulse. This signal simply cannot be taken out of the observations. Newton ignored it, Einstein put it in, and physics was revolutionized.

Event, signal, observer, this was the relationship which Einstein demonstrated as the fundamental unit in physics. "Relativity is the understanding of the world not as events but as relations." He put this immortal flash of insight into the language of mathematics, and presently was able to explain the erratic behavior of the planet Mercury—which Newtonian physics could not explain—and to predict the

bending of light near the sun. Later, his equation $E = mc^2$
was instrumental in producing the first atomic explosion.

Meanwhile Max Planck with quantum theory drastically
reversed the Newtonian idea about particles, and Heisenberg
announced the *principle of uncertainty*. Uncertainty gave
the world of science another shock, for it said that the universe and nature could not be described as a rigid mechanism of causes and effects. Take a chunk of uranium 235. A
small piece is unlikely to explode. A large piece is very likely
to explode. What is the critical size? This and similar questions have been answered with outstanding success by the
principle of uncertainty.

The generalist cannot be expected to follow the physics of
Einstein, Planck and Heisenberg in any detail—unless he
turn specialist—but he can readily understand how modern
physicists have outmoded the clockwork universe of Newton and Laplace, and replaced absolutes with relationships,
rigid cause and effect with processes, finalities with probabilities. He can understand that this revolution has proved
fruitful in the behavioral sciences as well as in the natural
sciences, and that relativity should armor every inquirer after
truth.

> What Einstein's principle of relativity states is that
> wherever you are in the universe . . . the same mathematical
> equations will suffice to describe your observations. I hope you
> will agree that this is a very powerful statement.

We laymen do agree, Mr. Fred Hoyle. Despite the inconceivable distances with which you present us, this statement
brings the universe somehow a little nearer. It is reassuring
to picture an intelligent being on one of the planets of Arc-
turus working with $E = mc^2$, quite like a professor in Tokyo
or Stockholm.

3 . The Solar System

AFTER ROVING around the billion-odd light years of the universe, the generalist returns to the solar system and finds it relatively cozy. Here are distances, sizes and rates which a normal mind can grasp, using simple arithmetic and English—or Spanish or Hindi. One could travel the 240,000 miles to the moon in a new taxi long before it wore out—assuming a road to travel on. The sun is 93 million miles away, and our fellow planets at negotiable distances. Pluto is the most remote, some 4 billion miles from the earth, a trip that would call for a whole fleet of taxis.

Where Pluto would be at a given moment requires a good deal of astronomical calculation, elementary perhaps for specialists. But even astronomers cannot train their senses to feel the dizzy speeds of our planet or its peripheral position in the galaxy. What comes naturally to the human nervous system is the Greek model. We can orient to the circling stars as long as they circle around the same point—preferably on this earth. Beyond that we must calculate, but by now most of us have the Copernican model well in mind.

How were the planets formed? Here, as in the formation of the universe, we find various speculative accounts: the nebular hypothesis of Laplace, the collision theory of Chamberlain—in which our sun smashes into another sun, and the planets develop from the matter thrown off. The preferred theory at present, however, is a refinement of the dust-cloud hypothesis. After the formation of the sun from a major dust cloud, so goes the theory, various smaller clouds were left floating in space. Some were pulled into the sun; others were far enough away to condense into separate bodies, which became the planets. The chief uncertainty about this hypothesis is how the condensations managed to maintain themselves during the early stages.

All of the current theories about the birth of stars and planets, says Fred L. Whipple, Harvard astronomer, leave a good deal to be desired. We are wandering in the haze of a trackless past. Perhaps, he says, an entirely new advance in science will be required to chart our way, and he quotes Hubble: "All of our ultimate problems demand that we acquire reliable information concerning distances, luminosities and masses. When these preliminary objectives are won, we shall turn to cosmological problems with new confidence."

AGE OF THE SOLAR SYSTEM

Have we confidence about the age of the solar system? Not a great deal, beyond the fact that it is to be measured in the billions. Based on recent studies of rocks and meteorites, its age works out somewhere between four and five billion years.

Observations at Mt. Wilson and Palomar tend to show that the sun is about halfway through its vigorous exercise of converting hydrogen into helium by thermonuclear reaction. Before it finishes the task, some billions of years hence, it is expected to swell to thirty times its present diameter, produce some very fancy fireworks, which will not be appreciated here, and gradually fade out to a white dwarf.

Whatever the facts about the creation and ultimate fate of the sun, its past, present and future effects on our planet are transcendent. Acting as a gigantic hydrogen reactor, 866,000 miles in diameter with a mass a million times that of the earth, it discharges continually into space colossal blasts of heat and radiation. The earth's atmosphere filters out the lethal ultraviolet and X rays which otherwise would bombard us. Without this protection we should soon die of acute sunburn or worse.

The tiny fraction of the total radiation of the sun which

falls on our small sphere accounts for our temperature, climate, our local forms of energy, our very life. If the heat radiated by the sun dropped no more than 13 per cent, the earth would presently be covered with an ice sheet a mile thick. If it rose 30 per cent, all life would be burned away. Thus the sun is indisputably the mother of us all. Sun-worshiping cults down the ages are quite understandable—in principle, if not in all their quaint practices.

Among its other gifts to the planet, the sun promotes the hydrologic cycle, pumping water from the oceans and returning it to the land as rain, and so maintains agriculture, as well as hydroelectric power. It is responsible for photosynthesis, the basic chemical process of plants, and thus in turn feeds all animal life. The sun, via plant and animal life, has produced in the past the beds of coal, the pools of oil and gas which now form our principal sources of energy. It gives promise of solar engines, which in future may even outstrip engines utilizing atomic fission—though perhaps not those that may utilize hydrogen fusion.

When H. G. Wells published his *Outline of History* a generation ago, astronomers pictured the solar system as slowly running down and cooling off. Some day, they said, our sun's heat would be so reduced that the earth's seas would freeze solid and life would end. As I write, in the late 1950's, specialists have veered to the other pole. Many see the sun getting hotter, as the fusion of hydrogen into helium works its way to the surface. Some day, they darkly extrapolate, it will become so jolly hot that the earth's seas will boil away, and we shall perish of heat, rather than cold.

At this point the generalist may wish that the astrophysicists would keep their extrapolations out of the headlines and in the family until they have reached at least a rough agreement. He wearies, too, of statistical calculations about a universe either expanding or contracting, like a puff adder.

JOURNEYS INTO SPACE

The sputniks now circling the earth have vastly increased the interest in space ships and trips to the moon, Mars and

beyond—an interest already lively, thanks to science fiction
and the manufacturers of plastic space helmets for children.
A Russian dog named Laika has lived in outer space for a
week, and we can be reasonably sure that presently a man
is going to try to do the same and attempt re-entry. What
can a generalist believe about journeys into space?

I think he should be pretty skeptical. A space trip even to
the moon presents a bristling series of difficulties. He must
picture himself in a thin shell of metal which may or may
not be correctly aimed, combating first the terrific heat
caused by the friction of the earth's atmosphere, and then
the bitter cold of space. He must avoid colliding with meteors, with showers of cosmic rays and other lethal types of
radiation, while maintaining confidence in the device which
furnishes him air to breathe.[1]

Colonel James P. Henry of the U.S. Air Force Research
Command, following a series of experiments, suggests that
the lack of accustomed *sensations* may constitute the most
serious problem of all. Under normal conditions the human
brain receives a constant flow of signals from the external
world, "feedbacks" which assure the mind that everything
is under control. Spacemen, cut off from this information
flow, the Colonel says, "might suffer a mental breakdown in
a few hours." Skiing once on a gray day, above the timber
line with no shadows to indicate ups or downs, and no clues
except in my feet and my speed, I caught a glimpse of what
the Colonel means. We are creatures of this earth, and to lose
even part of the earth's assurance is a sickening sensation.

Other problems include:

> Claustrophobia in a cramped space.
> Human-relations trouble with sealed-in companions.
> Descent to the surface of the moon without crashing.
> Armored suit and oxygen equipment to use on the moon.
> The blast-off from moon with proper aiming.

---

[1] US Explorer satellites have signaled back a new radiation, 1,000 times
more intense than cosmic rays, with a terrific heating effect. "It looks bad,"
says the *Scientific American* (June, 1958), "for space travellers."

Re-entry to earth's surface through air friction.
Problem of re-entry without crashing, and being promptly
discovered—or shall we say rescued?

Mars is the only other planet in our solar system which
may possibly support life. It has water and an atmosphere,
and may grow some form of lichens. Mercury and Venus,
nearer the sun than we, are much too hot for life as we know
it; Jupiter, Saturn, Uranus and Pluto, farther away, are much
too cold. The moon of course is dead. Thus to find living
things comparable to those we know, apparently we must
move to another solar system. The nearest star in our galaxy
is four light-years away, and all the taxis ever built would
wear out before they reached its planets, if it has any. They
would have to follow the course of a beam of light traveling
at 186,000 miles a second for four years.[2]

Are there intelligent beings in other solar systems? Fred
Hoyle guesses that there are at least a million planets in the
universe with intelligent life; Harlow Shapley guesses
100 million; biologists tend to be skeptical. The generalist
can put his money on any number he chooses. Personally, I
select no figure. Feeling reasonably sure that there are intelligent beings elsewhere in the universe, I salute them, and
hope they are doing better than we are.

Bertrand Russell sums it up: "I am afraid that, at any rate
for several centuries, we shall have to be content with our
planet as the only habitat for human beings."

SIGNALS COMING IN

Radio signals, it is reported, are coming in from beyond
the solar system. So far they seem random and meaningless.
Could they nevertheless have been encoded by intelligent
beings on some planet of another solar system in our galaxy?
Lancelot Hogben has suggested how such signals could be
exchanged, and a system of communication gradually
worked out, on the principle of the dots and dashes of the
Morse code.

---

2 $186,000 \times 60 \times 60 \times 24 \times 365 \times 4$, call it twenty-two quadrillion miles.

As for flying saucers from outer space, the generalist will be extremely skeptical. The sheer fact, says geneticist H. J. Muller, that in the tens of millions of years of life on earth no traces of such visitors have ever been found, strongly indicates the power of vast distances—twenty-two quadrillion miles at a minimum—in keeping us apart. A sound point; but the possibility of communication between worlds may hold brighter prospects.

The normal human mind is geared to deal with gross macroscopic events—land, water, weather, animals, plants, tools and artifacts—and can readily learn to perform simple arithmetic in respect to them. It is not geared to deal with either galaxies or atoms, the inconceivably great and the inconceivably small. To say that the sun is thirty thousand light-years from the center of the Milky Way sounds impressive, but the mind cannot really take it in. Without instruments astronomers could not have even guessed at the figure.

Again, to say that there are 10^{20} atoms on the point of a needle is not too remote from the medieval computation of the number of angels who could dance thereon, so far as ordinary meaning goes. Only by mastering higher mathematics, erecting technical models of events which are forever beyond sight or hearing, can humans hope to comprehend the universe in any detail.

Certain things, however, about the cosmos constitute useful knowledge for the generalist, and I have tried to outline them in this and the preceding chapter. We can put to one side the extrapolations about the way the universe will end, or the way the oceans of the earth will ultimately boil or freeze, and firmly grasp the high probability that, whatever the end may be for our globe, it is billions of years away. This, so far as practical plans for the future go, seems adequate.

If we do not blow ourselves up with foolish atomic experiments, or lay waste our resources like drunken sailors, we can be reasonably sure of a pleasant and stimulating home, in a hospitable universe, for a long time to come.

4 . Down to Earth

A SUPERSONIC jet at 1,000 miles an hour can fly a Great Circle around the earth in just over a day. Planes have greatly surpassed that speed for short flights. This world of ours is a small ball as planets go; to fly around Jupiter at 1,000 miles an hour would take 273 days. A man on foot, however, or in a sailing canoe, finds the earth reasonably roomy. Whether we traverse it at a thousand miles an hour or three, it is our only home.

Specialists concerned with studying the earth include geologists, geographers, meteorologists, seismographers (earthquake measurers), and others. Their specialties are often combined under the label the "earth sciences"—as anthropology, psychology, sociology, and so on, are labeled the "behavioral sciences."

The earth may have been formed, as we have noted, from minor dust and gas clouds billions of years ago, while the sun itself was forming from larger gas clouds. In its youth, scientists say, the earth went around the sun at a livelier pace than at present.

Three separate methods for dating meteorites agree on approximately 4.5 billion years for the age of the earth. "So strong and convincing was this converging of proofs that most scientists in the field concluded that the age had at last been reasonably well defined." [1] As late as 1903 it had been put at a mere 100 million years, subsequently increased by Lord Rutherford to 700 million years, then by others to 2 billion years. The generalist keeps an open mind for further estimates.

The surface of this embryonic whirling dust cloud gradually cooled and crusted over, under a gathering cloak of moisture such as now envelops Venus. At some point when conditions were right, the moisture condensed in torrential storms. It rained for centuries, in downpours beyond the power of even the Book of Genesis to describe, and filled the depressions in the rocky crust with shallow fresh-water seas. The salt came later, washed down by the rivers.

Repeated upheavals—due to internal heat, settling, volcanic action, the weight of the oceans, along with continual deluges—resulted in twisting the surface into many picturesque mountain ranges, deeply cut canyons, wild gorges, great basins and lakes. Rock was crushed into gravel and sand, essential to the plant life which was to come much later. For more than half of its existence, the earth has been as dead as the moon. The earth scientists have not yet worked out the exact sequence of this long period, and the generalist hardly need memorize the geologic detail of what is known.

He should realize clearly however that the earth is still a dynamic process, constantly changing its climate and its configurations. Seas cover old shores, and land pushes out of old seas, through the same sort of changes known earlier— volcanic eruptions, erosion, coral creatures indefatigably building, the gradual elevation of a continental shelf. Only the mass of the earth is relatively stable, "a closed system" geologists call it. Gravity holds the atmosphere in place, and what few particles escape are compensated by cosmic dust and meteors coming in. Conservationists who grieve over burning forests and eroded hills may find a little com-

---

[1] Ruth Moore: *The Earth We Live On* (Knopf, 1956).

fort in the thought that rain brings back the smoke-borne elements, and the sea may again return some of its silt to the land in a new upheaval from below the waters.

The moon itself, dead and barren as it is, adds to the earth's dynamism by ceaselessly pulling the tides back and forth. Where did the moon come from? Some scientists guess it was torn out of the earth itself, leaving a hole which became the Pacific Ocean. Others believe that it was the product of a still smaller dust cloud. It has practically no atmosphere, and no water. Doubts are now raised over the widely accepted theory that the craters on the moon were formed by volcanic action. A new school of astronomers speculates that they were formed by giant meteors smashing into the moon. If so, the layman asks, why have not more big meteors smashed into the earth? Perhaps they have, and their craters have been eroded away by wind and water, which the moon lacks.

Fred Hoyle makes the imaginative suggestion that if a mass of matter about the size, say, of the Mt. Everest massif should hit the moon at just the right angle, it might begin slowly to turn on its axis. What a rush to telescopes as we all tried to see what it was like on the back!

It is four thousand miles to the center of the earth, and scientists are disputing about what lies along the route. They agree that the crust on which we live is a "thin lamination," and that below it comes a rocky mantle some eighteen hundred miles thick. The composition of the inner core, however, whether solid or fluid, and the temperature variations below the crust are still unknown. We know far more about what goes on above our heads than below our feet.

To read the record of the rocks—a record obscured and in many places all but obliterated by eons of erosion and by concealing covers of sediments, lavas and invading seas—is a formidable program. Here is a gigantic palimpsest written in hieroglyph, and there is no Rosetta Stone by which to decipher it.[2]

---

[2] R. A. Daly in *Scientific American*, September, 1950.

Geologists have been working for generations to decipher this record. By 1900 they had demonstrated that the planet had a long history of relatively slow change, with cycles of erosion, sedimentation and mountain building. Young mountains are sharp and challenging to cragsmen, like the Rockies and Himalayas. Old mountains are worn down and rounded off, like the Appalachians and Laurentians of North America.

Nineteenth-century geologists divided the history of the rocks into Pre-Cambrian, Paleozoic, Mesozoic and Cenozoic eras. They had no clocks to measure by, but since 1900 a useful timekeeper has been found in radioactivity. This clock indicates that the oldest Pre-Cambrian rocks crystallized some two billion years ago, and it gives geologists a convenient scale, marked in ten-million-year periods, that has become one of the chief tools of the earth sciences.

ICE AGES

The earth is now enjoying an interval of relatively mild climate, as the last ice age retreats. We are in what is called an interglacial period. When the axis of the planet tilts a little and an ice age grips the earth, the area on which men can live shrinks drastically.[3] Twenty-five thousand years ago an ice sheet at least a mile thick covered Europe down to the center of what we now call England. It submerged North Germany and Poland, and stretched a frozen arm across Siberia. Another sheet ground its way across New England, down to the terminal moraine at Long Island, and a smaller ice cap centered in Switzerland. Mountain ranges everywhere were buried under far more ice and snow than at present. A vivid recollection of my boyhood is climbing the worn-down mountains of New Hampshire, while my father, an amateur geologist, pointed out the deep grooves which

---

[3] Tilting is one theory; changes in the amount of radiation from the sun, affecting the rate at which snow melts, is another. Some theorists postulate hot and cold eras alternating back for a billion years, depending on the sun's heat.

the last ice age had carved on granite ledges, and the huge boulders, some big as houses, it had dropped as it retreated.

Long after the first forms of life appeared, a procession of ice ages alternately contracted and expanded the space on which life was possible. (The only thing that lives on a high glacier is a glacier spider, unless you believe in the Abominable Snowman.) Though human history may be an irreversible process, the ice-age sequence is not unlikely to repeat itself. A fifth ice age could follow the four already identified. Note in this rough list that the glaciations are far from regular in their time span.

The *first ice age* spanned 60,000 years, beginning half a million years ago.[4]

The *first interglacial* followed, for a period of 50,000 years.

The *second ice age* ran for 140,000 years,

Followed by the *second interglacial,* 100,000 years.

The *third ice age* spanned 110,000 years, and

The *third interglacial,* a short one, only 20,000 years.

The *fourth ice age* ran from 120,000 to 12,000 years ago, and the

Fourth interglacial has now been with us for 12,000 years.

We are still in the warming-up phase.

We may have a little trouble as the fourth interglacial grows warmer, long before we start worrying about ice age number five. Former interglacials have become increasingly mild until the *polar ice caps have melted.* When they melt, they release enough locked-up water to raise ocean levels around the world a hundred feet or more. Ancient beaches are identified far up present hillsides. The next time you look at your favorite beach, imagine it under a hundred

---

4 A recent technique of calculating deep ocean temperatures in past ages indicates that the ice ages may not have begun so far back (*Scientific American,* February, 1958).

feet of water. Florida would largely disappear, Manhattan
Island would be submerged save for skyscrapers, and San
Francisco reduced to a cluster of islands. This is not, be it
noted, one of those gay astronomical extrapolations; this is
no fooling, based on the past performance of three interglacials.

The fifth ice age, if it comes, will send its glaciers down
into Europe, Asia and North America again, and freeze up
enough water to lower ocean levels once more. Men lived
through the last one by moving south ahead of the ice, along
with the game. Our descendants can doubtless survive future glaciations, with ocean levels up and down, but to preserve a high-energy civilization with population in the
billions will require some pretty careful planning.

THE "THIN LAMINATION"

We are confined on the earth's surface on a thin lamination between the insulating atmosphere overhead, and the
solid, almost impenetrable earth underfoot. The atmosphere
is opaque to all but a narrow band of radiation that trans-
mits light and heat, and a little wider band that permits
penetration of very short radio waves.

As one goes up through the thinning atmosphere it grows
colder; as he goes down through the almost impenetrable
ground—in deep mines for instance—it grows hotter. A few
miles down comes an intolerable furnace; a few miles up
comes an approach to absolute zero—or so most specialists
believe.

To learn more about what is above and below, many
ingenious studies are constantly being made, a great number during the International Geophysical Year. Earth satellites have been blasted into outer space, while observers
around the world, armed with instruments, decode the messages they send. We shall see more stirring photographs of
our planet and hear strange new radio signals from outer
space. Some entirely novel areas of knowledge are being
opened up.

The surface of the earth is covered by two and one-half times as much salt water as land, while half of the land is rendered practically uninhabitable by polar ice, tundra, swamps, mountain ranges, desert, rain forests. Brazil is larger than the United States, but much of it lies in the equatorial jungles of the Amazon, where life is too luxuriant for civilized man. (Those spirited females, the Amazons, alas are only an exhibit in anti-knowledge.) Most of the world's civilizations have flourished in the North Temperate Zone, where citizens are not obliged to spend so much of their energy trying to keep warm or cool.

We live and breathe in an ocean of air—pressing down on every person with an unnoticed weight of several tons —an ocean which obviously must remain clean. During the last half century, carbon dioxide, man-made dust storms, smog, fall-out from atomic explosions have increasingly polluted the ocean above us. Since the advent of agriculture, men have always distorted their local environment; now for the first time they are beginning to clutter up the environment of the whole globe.

Among other matters investigated in the Geophysical Year is the effect of the huge amounts of carbon dioxide discharged into the atmosphere from the combustion of coal and oil. As industrialization goes up, so does carbon dioxide, while fuel reserves go down. What is the effect on the weather? What is the carbon-dioxide layer doing to our cities? Smog, a mixture of smoke and fog, is blamed for killing many persons in a Pennsylvania coal town, and it is a growing threat to Los Angeles and to other industrialized and motorized communities.

Until recent times our thin lamination had hardly any thickness at all—the two-dimensional surface of the earth upon which people traveled and breathed. Now we have made it a little less thin. A balloon with a man in a pressurized cabin has risen twenty miles in the air. Bathyspheres are carrying observers several miles into the dark depths of the sea, while the deepest mines penetrate about the same distance into the close, hot crust of the earth. Thus today the lamination is at the most twenty-five miles thick.

Despite severe earthquakes and volcanic eruptions from time to time, the threat to survival from below seems a good deal less than the man-made threat from above.

MAPS FOR THE EARTH SCIENCES

We keep track of our thin lamination by making maps— aided nowadays by aerial photography. Useful maps for generalists should begin not with nations and political divisions—the British Empire all in red—but with continents, oceans, islands, rivers, mountain ranges, deserts, ice sheets, jungles, forests, pampas.

Next should come maps of water resources, minerals, crop land, transportation and trade routes. One map should show the races of mankind, and another the areas of the great religions. Civilized regions could be contrasted with areas still occupied by nature peoples—some of them, in New Guinea for instance, still in the Stone Age.

National frontiers would come almost last, with the warning that such maps are subject to change without notice. The political maps of Asia, Africa and Europe have shifted fantastically since John Gunther wrote his books about them. Politicians have recently relocated the boundaries of India, but not the Himalaya mountains.

The International Geographical Union has been making a land-use map of the world, which could be used to keep our homestead in better order, and to correct some of the economic monstrosities which result from political decisions. Let us follow a modern geographer, George H. T. Kimble, who offers a few striking examples.[5]

The great African peanut-oil program of the British government after the war cost taxpayers thirty million pounds and proved a disastrous loss. Why? Because its promoters

---

[5] In *Frontiers of Knowledge*. See bibliography.

did not have adequate maps of Tanganyika; they did not know enough about its climate, rainfall, contours, soils and available labor force. By way of contrast, reliable maps of England *were* available when that country was forced to grow more food to survive in World War II. The potential acreage for crops was clearly shown, and the food supply presently was doubled.

Japan today, says Kimble, makes very little economic sense. Her population has increased from thirty million in 1894 to more than ninety million—Tokyo is now the largest city in the world—while her areas for crops and mineral resources have declined, and her foreign trade has been severely limited compared with exports and imports before the war.

Even a layman, after one glance at the map, can see that the new state of Pakistan constitutes an economic monstrosity, split as it is in two widely separated parts.

Without adequate maps, Kimble observes, "Point Four" programs for foreign aid by the United Nations, or by the United States, can do more harm than good. It is dangerous to upset established economic and social patterns, however inefficient they may seem, he says, until new patterns to take their place have been carefully designed.

Kimble emphasizes that despite the fruitfulness and the diversity of the planet's natural resources, there are certain stern limitations. For instance, there is not enough metal to provide every human family with a six-room house, a car, a refrigerator and a TV set. It can be done perhaps for North America and Europe, but any attempt to supply the world would exhaust known iron and copper deposits in a few years.

There is not enough arable land in the world to supply the present population of 2.7 billion people with the diet enjoyed by the 190 million in the United States and Canada. Sufficient calories can be supplied, but not in the form of meat. Meat requires land and labor to grow the food for the animals, and then more land and labor to process the meat—an operation which doubles the cost. Kimble is confident that we have the technical knowledge to feed, house and clothe the present population adequately, but not to supply them with high-powered cars, split-level houses and other items of the American standard of living. World standards simply cannot be based on the present material goals of North Americans.

PLANETARY HOUSEKEEPING

In addition to man-made trouble from overhead, there is trouble on the surface too, some of it long-standing. Before the first cities, neolithic herdsmen domesticated sheep and goats, animals very proficient in manufacturing deserts by eating all seedling trees. Specialists believe that it was these unfenced grazing herds which turned large areas of the Middle East and North Africa into desert.

Almost any knowledge about our earthly home is worth having, and there are various ways to get it, including simple observation. On a train from the Midwest to New York the other day, I took some housekeeping notes on the conditions to the south of the railroad tracks. Among the items I noted through the train window were:

> Croplands showing erosion—sheet, finger and gulley—in sections not protected by contour plowing. Erosion means a progressive decrease of fertility.
>
> Rivers and streams yellow with silt, some of them polluted with sewage. The silt is another result of man-made erosion.
>
> Blackened stumps left by forest fires.
>
> Surface mines and gravel pits—yawning craters surrounded by slag heaps.
>
> Urban and rural slums, with unsightly dumps on their margins.

Some of this waste and ugliness is unavoidable in the transition from a low-energy culture to a high, but certainly it is no way for a permanent, pleasant homeland to look. It can be duplicated in whole or in part wherever industrialism has gripped a society. For most of my train ride both the majesty of the wilderness and the charm of a handicraft civilization had disappeared.

There is still enough food in the planetary larder, but not necessarily forever. In Indiana I saw mile-long fields of tall ripening corn, but even these may not remain as healthy as they look. Large-scale farms are notoriously easy marks for pests and fungi, which may turn into epidemics to sweep a whole region. Lacking the checks and balances of wild nature, big farms call for the services of specialists who spend their time fighting the growing hordes of pests. Nature keeps matters under control by intermingling a wide variety of plants, but man, with his uniform seas of corn or wheat, gives pests a field day, in more senses than one.

It is hard to destroy the majesty of the Hudson River Valley, though with gas tanks, dumps, billboards and factories we have done our best. The bridges across the Hudson, however, are quite worthy of the majestic setting. By the time my train entered the chaos north of New York, I was ready to declare that the most important thing a generalist should know about the earth was how to clean up the mess we have made of it.

Then my mind turned to that photograph taken from a rocket, a hundred miles up—perhaps the most stirring picture I have ever looked at—with the American Southwest seen through a lacework of clouds, the Colorado River entering the Gulf of California, and the Pacific Ocean beyond, curving with the great curve of the earth. The clutter and waste were gone. Only the noble outline remained.

5 . Somehow Life Begins

MOST EDUCATED PEOPLE in Europe and the Americas a hundred years ago believed with Bishop Ussher that all life on earth began in the year 4004 B.C. In that year the world had been created from a "firmament in the midst of the waters," and a few days later the plants, the creatures and Adam and Eve were placed in their appropriate environments, fully developed.

Three lines of scientific inquiry converged, about 1860, to demolish this romantic picture, and move creation back by millions of years. A long, complicated process of slow change in living things was substituted for the sudden appearance of the finished product. Darwin in 1859 published *The Origin of Species,* which outlined the tremendous story of evolution. Sir Charles Lyell in 1863 published *The Antiquity of Man,* which presented the accumulated evidence of geology about the ages of rocks, fossils, and life on land and in the seas. Archaeologists, who had been digging up layer after layer of bones, pottery and artifacts in the caves of France and Spain, produced incontrovertible evidence that men as well as animals existed long before 4004 B.C.

The Western world might have evaded any one of these arguments, at least for a time, but the three together could not be dismissed. Scientists and intelligent laymen were forced to construct a new cosmic picture, utterly different from what they had been brought up to believe. Darwin especially struck a shattering blow at the human ego by demonstrating man's close relationship to other animals. No such intellectual shock had been felt since Copernicus removed the earth from the center of the universe. Copernicus dealt with space, Darwin and Lyell with time; the concept of space-time was yet to come.

It is hard for us today to imagine the general bewilderment. I caught a glimpse of it in reading my grandfather's journals, with their running commentary in a precise copperplate hand. Reared as a religious fundamentalist, but with an inquiring mind, he read Darwin and Herbert Spencer. Only after a long, hard battle with his soul did he eventually join the First Unitarian Church of Haverhill, Massachusetts. Christians were the most shaken by the new knowledge, but members of other sects were astonished too.

What Darwin demonstrated, observes H. J. Muller, is still not well understood by laymen. We must, he says, "overcome this dangerous blindness concerning what we ourselves are, what we came from and how, where we now stand, and where we are headed for." Julian Huxley sounds a similar note: "I hold strongly that without some knowledge of evolution one cannot hope to arrive at a true picture of human destiny, or even to approach the problem correctly." Obviously we enter here an area of great significance to generalists. Let us try to block it roughly in.

THE BEGINNINGS OF LIFE

All forms of living things on earth, viruses, plants, animals and man, had their beginnings in the warm, shallow seas of two billion years ago. Since the planet's age as we have noted is now estimated at something more than four billion years, life has thus been in evidence for about half the time.

Specialists are pretty well agreed that the sea contained the necessary mineral salts to form organic molecules—nitrates and probably ammonium compounds. At just the right temperature, with radiation from the sun through perhaps a thinner atmosphere than today, a chance assembly of such molecules apparently formed a living particle able to feed and grow and reproduce itself. This particle, extremely complex compared with inorganic matter, was simple compared with even a single living cell. It may have resembled a virus, or as some authors describe it, a "naked gene." It increased rapidly, in the nourishing culture medium of the sea water. In due time it developed into a cell, with a wall and a nucleus, and proceeded to manufacture copies of itself.

This is the essence of living matter, an arrangement of chemicals capable of reproducing the pattern—originally by simple division, later by the mechanisms of sex. Most scientists agree that the earliest living structure was a microscopic water plant, a simple form of green alga, that animals came eons later, and that living things did not push or crawl up on land until about 300 million years ago. The first mammals appeared some 70 million years back, and true man not more than 250,000 years ago.

All very interesting; but how did the warm soup of sea water, organic molecules and radiation suddenly produce a living particle with the remarkable power of reproducing itself? Nobody knows, and nobody will ever know for sure until the transformation is produced in the laboratory—an event unlikely in the near future, in spite of occasional rumors, but ultimately not inconceivable.

THREE ALTERNATIVES

Another question: Why doesn't life spontaneously appear today following the same formula—whatever the formula may be—say along the margins of the Red Sea or the Caribbean? Can we be sure it does not? Julian Huxley has an answer. He suggests that bacteria would gobble up the soft, defenseless protoplasm. When life originated, there were no bacteria by definition; this form of life came later in the timetable.

Huxley sets before us three logical alternatives:

1. Life was created by some supernatural agency.
2. It was brought to earth from outer space—for instance by a meteor.
3. It developed naturally out of inorganic materials, at just the right temperatures and radiations.

As a scientist he dismisses the first alternative. To accept it would put him back with Bishop Ussher. He raises a large question mark over the second alternative; even the toughest virus could hardly withstand the cold of outer space, or the terrific heat generated by friction when a meteor enters the earth's atmosphere.

Most intelligent laymen will follow Huxley and select the third alternative—a natural, repeatable development from inorganic matter. Logic then carries us on to a further speculation. We know that the chemical elements and energies found on earth are present throughout the universe. If there is life on Mars, if there are sentient beings on planets in other solar systems, they probably originated in the same manner as on earth, and developed gradually from a simple cell into more and more complex forms.

Did the early cells have the indomitable energy that we see in living things today? One stands on the rocky summit of a New England mountain and looks at the margin where tree gives way to shrub, shrub to herb, herb to a carpet of moss, and moss to granite. One looks again at the granite ledge, to find it spotted with lichens; life is attacking the core material of the earth itself. Or one looks in September at a pole-bean vine that was a single hard dry seed in May, and gives up trying to calculate by how many thousand per cent it has multiplied itself. One thinks of uncounted billions of coral animals which have built up the Great Barrier Reef of Australia.

The generalist, despite his natural curiosity, does not really need to know exactly how life began. He needs to know in broad outline how it has developed from that beginning, where it seems to be going, and where the human race fits in. It will doubtless be quite an occasion when a viruslike substance, capable of copying itself, is produced in some laboratory in Ann Arbor or Leningrad. A world-wide holiday would be in order! It is safe to predict, however, that no laboratory will ever be able to duplicate the course of natural selection beyond a very elementary stage.

ORIGIN OF SPECIES

The original cell must have copied itself in a kind of geometrical progression until an appreciable area was occupied. How did new types of cells and new species arise? Darwin sought the answer in *The Origin of Species,* and found it—to the consternation of my grandfather.

A new species appears when a section of the original species encounters a different environment, calling for different behavior, and gradually changes its characteristics until it can no longer interbreed with the original. A swarm of primordial cells might drift into colder water, or into a separate lagoon. There the cells must adjust to new conditions or die. They manage to adjust, and after enough generations, a new species is born. All manner of happenings speed the process: a different pool, a heavier rainfall, a drought, shifting food supply, new enemies. The long tongues of an ice age could split a species.

As a species multiplies down the ages, it produces countless small variations, in what specialists call the "genetic pool." The differing combinations of genes, assured by the sexual process, change with each generation. They produce for instance the intricate patterns in the fur of a cat, or the brilliant plumage of a male grosbeak, to be reinforced by the admiring choices of the females.

Sometimes, however, a new species develops suddenly by mutation—a cataclysmic event to which we will return presently. Gradual adjustment, through minute variations over eons, to a changing environment, and sudden mutation: these two broadly account for the origin of species.

FROM SEA TO LAND

Life began in the sea, and scientists estimate that 90 per cent of the chemical transformations of life still occur under water. After colonies of cells form, they presently begin to organize the work of living—some to eat, others to move about, still others to reproduce. The sponges began in some such way. Animals originated as plants which learned to move about. Some species even today, like the Ascidians, Volvox, Euglena, are part plant, part animal.

After a billion and more years of evolution under water, a rich variety of plants, animals, plant-animals and bacteria populated the seas. Some species had grown hard shells, which left a record on the rocks; the earliest fossils so far known are dated 500 million years ago.

How did living things emerge from the seas to breathe oxygen directly, rather than dissolved in water? One theory is that the rise and fall of the tides gradually toughened little sea plants on tidal margins to survive in the air for a few hours. After many generations of such adaptation they evolved into a new species. They could now live permanently out of water, and proceeded to spread up the beaches and cliffs.

After the landfall of plants, how did land animals begin? Julian Huxley develops one interesting theory. About 300 million years ago, he says, primitive lungfish with swim bladders were living in fresh-water lakes. The climate grew drier and the lakes shrank to pools. The fish was forced to wobble painfully on its fins from one pool to another, hoarding a deep gulp of air in its lung. After a long period of this arduous operation, the lungfish evolved into a clumsy land animal.

Specialists have so far identified more than a million sea and land animals, including insects, and more than 300,000 species of plants. There may be as many more alive today and not identified, while an untold number have become extinct. The species now on file range from a virus, barely visible with the help of an electronic microscope, to a whale, the biggest living animal,[1] and a redwood tree, the biggest living thing there is, as well as the oldest.

From polar regions to the equator, says Julian Huxley, from high mountains to the depths of the sea, from hot springs, just below the boiling point, to the airless interior of other animals, life exploits the environment in every possible way. Animals feed on wood, feathers, on nectar, excrement and another's living intestines, as well as on plants and flesh.

It is fascinating to follow the many lines of development leading to the forms we catalogue today. We reflect, for instance, on the failure of the dinosaurs to survive; on how birds got into a kind of evolutionary blind alley by sacrificing front legs for wings; how flowering plants, with their seeds incased in nutriment, completed the cover of the land, gave it color, and provided food for new kinds of animals. Without flowers, says Eiseley, no mammal and no man could ever have been developed—a truly poetic thought.[2] Many specialists devote their lives to following one twig on one branch of the tree of life.

NATURAL SELECTION

There is an old story that a laboratory man cut off the tails of mice, generation after generation, trying to find out if acquired characteristics—no tails—could be inherited. Despite the repeated surgery, the last generation had tails as long as the first. I find this story helpful in remembering the principle of natural selection.

I remember too what happened to flies in my garage when I tried to eliminate them with DDT. Most of the flies died, but a few mysteriously survived. Presently there were more, obstinately impervious to spraying. I had apparently encouraged the breeding of flies able to resist DDT. As the

---

[1] Probably the biggest animal which ever lived. It may weigh up to a hundred tons.

[2] Loren Eiseley: *The Immense Journey* (Random House, 1957).

resisters bred, their offspring grew even more resistant. I was caught in the majestic law of natural selection, and my experience has been widely confirmed. By the 1950's, localities in New York, New Hampshire, Florida, Texas, Italy, Sweden reported that DDT was no longer effective. Other localities, however, reported 100 per cent effectiveness. Citrus growers using hydrocyanic gas for pests have been forced to employ ever stronger solutions, while firms manufacturing the gas no longer guarantee success.

Where is that fabulous dinosaur, the Tyrannosaurus, perhaps the most ferocious creature ever developed on this earth? No men were around to spray him with chemicals, but similar principles were at work. Instead of the challenge of DDT, he had to meet the challenge of a relatively rapid decline in his food supply, and like the flies in some localities, he failed to meet it.

Natural selection causes those individuals who have the genetic equipment to adapt to a change, to survive and mate. Their offspring, following Mendel's laws of heredity, will be even better adapted. My few selected houseflies were so equipped, the whole dinosaur tribe was not. The unequipped die off, the fittest survive. Observe that this has nothing to do with a "struggle" between houseflies, it has only to do with the arrangement of genes as they vary from one individual fly to another. If the environment, natural or man-made, shifts too swiftly for the genes to handle, the individual, sometimes the whole species, will disappear. What would happen to the anteater if the ants up and left?

Severing tails, on the contrary, has no effect on the genes. The way to get a strain of short-tailed mice is to put a lot of them in an environment which penalizes long-tailedness —traps, for instance, which catch long tails. Those with shorter tails will survive and mate. Given time and generations enough, tails will come down. This is the method that animal and plant breeders have followed for thousands of years: if you want a race horse, breed from the fastest mares

and stallions. It has been done by trial and error, without
the scientific help of Darwin, Mendel, or Thomas Hunt
Morgan, but it has worked. The extreme example, of course,
is the dog. He was originally bred from a wild foxlike animal, but now ranges from an Irish wolfhound, weighing
150 pounds, to a 1-pound Mexican hairless.

CHROMOSOMES AND GENES

The generalist should have a broad knowledge of the
principles of heredity. Most people, including some very
intelligent people, have missed the point. They carry around
two serious misconceptions: *first,* that a son inherits his
father's unique characteristics; *second,* that the "survival of
the fittest" always means the survival of the strong and ruthless—a misconception which suggests some rash and untenable conclusions about human nature and human society.

Genes are the irreducible units of inheritance in bacteria,
plants, animals and man. A fruit fly has about five thousand
genes, a man vastly more. They are all different, and neatly
arranged in a larger unit called a chromosome. A new individual begins when egg cell and sperm cell fuse to form *one*
cell, which always contains two sets of chromosomes, one
set from each parent. The cell then begins to divide, taking
its chromosomes along, and with a powerful microscope we
can watch the division in certain living plants. It proceeds
"in as orderly and complex a ritual as a courtly eighteenth
century ballet." [3] Literally, the dance of life; I have a dia-
gram of it here on the desk before me.

A human child receives a set of chromosomes, with its
neatly packaged genes, from his father and a set from his
mother—but not the same set which gave his parents *their*
characteristics. The parents in turn have received sets from
their parents, and so on back, and in the complex interrela-
tions many of the genes lie dormant. Specific genes give
the child his personal characteristics—say blond hair, or
hemophilia, or brown skin, or a predisposition to hay fever.

---

[3] A. E. Mirsky in the *Scientific American Reader.* See bibliography.

No one can predict all the traits he will inherit, or analyze where they came from. Biologists call the stronger traits *dominant*, the weaker traits *recessive*.

A boy baby will *not* inherit his father's alcoholism or ability to write poetry. If later on he takes to drink or poetry it will be by imitating his father, thus a cultural, not an inherited, trait. Culture is what we learn *after* we are born; inheritance is *what we are born with*. Despite the apparent conviction of many novelists to the contrary, characteristics acquired during one lifetime, like severed mice tails, cannot be inherited. Some traits of feeling and temperament are very probably inherited, but this is hard to demonstrate, because association in the family reinforces such traits.

Gregor Mendel, who in the 1860's worked out the statistical law by which characteristics are inherited, stands a towering scientific figure, along with Darwin. His report was neglected for many years, but by 1900 its great importance was recognized. Mendel, a Catholic monk, crossed the strains of garden peas with white and pink flowers. After recording many generations, he found that an average of one-quarter of the grandchildren will have white flowers, and three-quarters pink. Combining whites will give only white; combining pinks will give both pink and white, again in the ratio of three to one. Pink is the "dominant" characteristic in this case, white the "recessive." All living things, he proceeded to generalize, will have dominant and recessive characteristics which obey this statistical law. In Homo sapiens, black skin is dominant, white skin recessive. A good many tragedies in race relations might have been averted, had people better understood Mendel's law.

SURVIVAL AND ADAPTATION

Now let us examine the misconception about the "survival of the fittest." It is true that there is a struggle, sometimes a lethal one, between species, as any tropical jungle bears witness. It is true that sometimes the strongest and most ruthless members of a given species survive. But it was

not the strongest and most belligerent flies which survived
in my garage; it was those that could best resist DDT. Nor
was there any fighting among the flies as to which would
survive; the situation was of a quite different order. Homo
sapiens well illustrates the difference. He has genes foster-
ing a big brain, and by its use he can master and trap a mammoth or a gorilla. No animal however strong and ruthless
can withstand him if he carefully plans its capture.

Economists in the nineteenth century used to talk a good
deal of nonsense about the survival of the fittest. They said
that Darwin's principles of evolution supported the principle of *laissez faire;* namely, that the best businessman was
the one who could successfully overwhelm his competitors.
This was a perversion of the theory of evolution. The survival of the fittest does not necessarily mean the most ruthless; it does not necessarily favor the strong. *It favors those
individuals with genes capable of surviving change in environment.* Sometimes it may be the meek who have the
best chance.

We should also grasp the important difference between
adaptability and adaptation. Man, as noted earlier, is the
most adaptable of all earth's creatures. He can live near the
poles like the Eskimos, or near the equator like Amazonian
Indians. He can shift with the advancing and retreating ice
ages. Creatures which are perfectly adapted to a given environment, on the contrary, are more vulnerable. When
glaciers advance, or oceans recede, or rainfall declines, they
die out. For years a great colony of sea gulls lived on the refuse of the St. Augustine shrimp fleet in Florida. When the
fleet suddenly moved away, most of the gulls had forgotten
how to fish for themselves and perished.

Darwin did not invent evolution—the idea was known to
his grandfather as an unconfirmed theory. But Darwin, like
Newton, had the ability to fit the pieces of previous knowledge together. He analyzed the machinery of evolution, and
named it natural selection. He said that evolution is ex-

plained if we assume that environment causes better-adapted organisms to survive. When once Darwin proposed this chain of causes and effects, it was accepted by nearly all thoughtful persons. Minds filled with preconceptions—like the mind of William Jennings Bryan—rejected it.

NOTE ON MUTATIONS

We have briefly touched on some outstanding headings in the great epic of life—its beginnings, the emergence from the sea, natural selection and the origin of species, Mendel's law, the survival of the fittest. A word about mutations is in order, especially as it bears on the serious modern threat of atomic fall-out.

The origin of a new species is usually a slow, drawn-out process, requiring many generations, sometimes eons. But occasionally a new species appears overnight by mutation, a kind of "cataclysmic evolution." A rose with fourteen chromosomes suddenly produces an offspring with twenty-eight; a tobacco plant with twenty-four doubles to forty-eight. The new variety cannot be crossed with the parent, but will breed true. This can happen, we are told, with all forms of life. *Why* does it happen? Darwin never explained for he knew little about mutations.

One theory is that the genes of the parent have been exposed to radiation; they may have been hit, for instance, by a cosmic ray coming from outer space. Once at the Barthol Foundation laboratories in Swarthmore, Pennsylvania, I listened to a Geiger counter as it registered cosmic rays. They came irregularly, click, click, click-click, click—averaging about one a second. The physicists there assured me that my body was being drilled by cosmic rays at the same rate—and so was every living thing on earth.

The Brookhaven Laboratories of the Atomic Energy Commission are forcing experimental mutations on a wide variety of plants. Radiation from cobalt 60 is developing new species of potatoes, apples, corn, wheat, carnations. Samples come in to Brookhaven for analysis from all over the world.

Plants near the radiation source mostly die; further away astonishing monsters are created. Most mutations are harmful, decreasing the chance of survival. A few beneficial mutations, however, are turning up at Brookhaven. Dr. Calvin Konzak, working on cereals, has developed strains which resist such destructive plant diseases as Victoria blight and stem rust. Brookhaven may ultimately give us new varieties of food.

We can be sure, however, that when atomic radiation hits human beings, especially their reproductive organs, it will cause an unpleasant variety of mutations. The resulting monsters will be more painful to contemplate than any perverted vegetables at Brookhaven. The monster making has already begun, and every new explosion increases the hazard. The delayed fall-out from H-bombs will bring added dangers, as it sifts through the atmosphere year after year.

THE CYCLE OF PHOTOSYNTHESIS

All the animals on land and in the sea, including man, are but a small brood of parasites living off the great body of the plant kingdom. So far as we know, green plants alone are able to produce the stuff of life—proteins, sugars, fats—from the stable inorganic materials, with no help but the abundantly flowing light of the sun.[4]

The last is the miraculous process called photosynthesis. Each year, Dr. Rabinowitch goes on to say, the plants of land and sea combine some 150 billion tons of carbon with 25 billion tons of hydrogen, to set free 400 billion tons of oxygen. In endlessly repeated cycles, atoms of carbon and hydrogen leave the earth's air and water, to enter into living things by photosynthesis. "After a tour of duty that may last seconds or millions of years in the unstable organic world, they return to the stable equilibrium of inorganic nature." In beds of coal and pools of oil the organic atoms may be on duty for eons. As you run your car, you return these atoms to nature's more stable equilibrium.

---

[4] E. I. Rabinowitch in the *Scientific American Reader*. See bibliography.

Is there anything in the mythology of any country, from the Greeks to the Javanese, to equal this majestic saga? Even the hydrologic cycle, where the earth's waters are lifted by the sun to fall as rain and run to the seas again, cannot compare with it. In this vast cycle of photosynthesis, inorganic atoms enter into the stuff of life, become enmeshed in its complex structure. After seconds, or centuries, they revert to inorganic nature, to lie barren or repeat the process.

Contemplating the drama of this transformation, the generalist can glimpse a new dimension in understanding, where the line between "animate" and "inanimate" begins to fade and "living things become a part of the continuum of matter and energy, as natural as the galaxies."

Atoms of various elements [5] combine into the molecules of the stuff with which we mostly deal outside the laboratory —air, water, wood, soil, minerals, food. Inorganic molecules are usually simple; the H_2O of water is one of the simplest. The molecules of living things are far more complicated— but their atomic material is the same. The protein molecule of milk is written: $C_{1864}H_{3012}O_{576}N_{468}S_{21}$, a combination of carbon, hydrogen, oxygen, nitrogen and sulfur.

Organic molecules are always ready to combine with oxygen. Such oxidations, says Rabinowitch, are the mainspring of life, without which "no heart could beat, no plant could grow upward defying gravity, no amoeba could swim, no sensation spread along a nerve, no thought could flash in a human brain."

Radioactivity may turn out to be an essential part of the process of life, and specialists are constantly learning more about it. Take the quite recent discovery of carbon 14, which has been put to practical use in dating archaeological finds, as we shall presently see. All organic life contains some of this radioactive carbon, which decays so slowly, over cen-

---

5 There are 92 elements known in nature, from hydrogen, the lightest, to uranium, the heaviest. Scientists are now industriously creating new elements, never seen on land or sea, of which plutonium is the most famous.

turies and millennia, that it offers clues today to events before the ice ages. The shorter radioactivity of other elements in living matter of course ticks away much faster and disappears; but a small-scale process of atomic fission may go on in every living plant and animal. The generalist may look for new discoveries along this line, and soon.

DAWN OF INTELLIGENCE

Man is a reasoning animal, but by no means the only one. Were it not for language, he might be only a little smarter than a chimpanzee—though still considerably smarter than a bird, an ant or a honey bee. The greatest improvement ever made in the machinery of life was the nervous system, leading to a controlling brain. Protozoa and sponges have no nervous structure—only a simple but still unexplained sensitive response. Polyps, such as the sea anemone, show a primitive nervous system, though messages along their nerve channels are slow.

Primitive creatures respond to the environment by inherited patterns—like moths flying into the light. Over the eons, natural selection favored creatures which could make choices; should they run, or stand their ground? A nervous system capable of carrying rapid messages, together with a memory system, gave them the power of choice, based on past experiences, and a higher survival value.

The ability to reflect and refer to memory evolved in certain species of spiders, crustaceans, squids, and presently in mammals. This multiple rise of intelligence, H. J. Muller believes, "gives ground for inferring that it has evolved on other worlds as well as our own." Given the necessary chemical elements and the living cell, evolution is probably bound to take this course—namely, away from purely instinctive behavior toward more reflective and intelligent behavior. "Conceptual thought and imagination only represent the most advanced degree of development."

When mammals first appeared on earth, some seventy million years ago, family troubles began. The young were born utterly helpless and, unlike young fishes, needed a lot of nursing and attention. Observe your cat and her newborn kittens. The ability to learn from experience now acquired a high biological premium. Natural selection meanwhile promoted an increase in relative head size and brain size, accelerating the process.

A Darwin from a distant planet, visiting the earth at the time, might have confidently predicted the emergence of man.

6 . And Man Arrives

TO LOCATE the first human being in time and space is as impossible as to locate the first living cell.

Mammals came on the scene about seventy million years ago, as we have noted. After some fifty million years more of natural selection a primitive apelike creature was evolved. From his descendants, various species fanned out, some to become extinct, others to evolve into monkeys, into the great apes, and into man. Most biologists today do not believe that Homo sapiens is descended from monkeys, but that he *shares* with monkeys and the great apes (the gorilla, orang-utan, chimpanzee and gibbon) a common ancestor. The ape clans are our cousins, not our forebears.

This ancestor was at least as intelligent as other mammals, in that he could learn from experience. Unlike most other mammals, moreover, he learned to stand erect and walk after he had come down from the trees—although there is some question about his being a tree dweller to begin with. An erect posture is a major characteristic of man; most monkeys go on all fours; the apes shamble rather than walk. Standing erect frees the hands for manipulating sticks, stones, and ultimately tools. Birds stand erect, of course, but have exchanged hands for wings. We pay a price for our posture, however, in backaches, slipped discs, increased difficulty of childbirth, hernias and circulation troubles—since our pump is four feet off the ground.

An even more important characteristic was the development of language. Most students now believe that this faculty chiefly distinguishes Homo sapiens from all other forms of life. Many animals communicate by cries, growls, grunts, dances (as in the honey bee reporting the position of nectar to the hive), but no other animal has developed inflected language, which in turn bestows the power of abstract thought. Words of course are not transmitted through the genes, but the biological machinery for speech is so transmitted.

FAMILY TREE

The family tree of man runs roughly as follows:

1. Devonian lungfish—perhaps the first animal to come ashore, 300 million years ago.

2. Reptiles, developed by natural selection, and then

3. Mammals, appearing 70 million years ago.

4. Primates—developing perhaps 20 million years ago into that common ancestor of man and apes.

5. Anthropoids found in South Africa, with characteristics of both man and ape—a relatively small creature with a small brain, but walking upright.

6. Proto-men, with larger brains and bodies. They learned to kindle fire and shape rough tools. "Peking" man, "Java" man, "Heidelberg" man, belong here, the names denoting where their bones were found. Their skulls show jutting brows and a shortage of chin.

7. True men, appearing perhaps as much as 250,000 years ago, though more fossils for dating are badly needed. They seem to have appeared rather suddenly. As they lived in bands, they required a communication system.

Our direct ancestors, these true men, must have dragged out a miserable existence through the ice ages. With the retreat of the last glaciation, however, they developed strong migratory impulses. They roamed over the Old World from the Volga to Malaya to the Cape of Good Hope. They crossed

Bering Strait—with ocean levels probably down—into
Alaska, overran North America, and ultimately worked their
way down to Tierra del Fuego, the jumping-off place of
human existence, as Darwin describes it in *The Voyage of
the Beagle*.

Nobody knows within thousands of years when proto-man
evolved into true man, but we know that four things must
have happened before Homo sapiens appeared: [1]

1. His brain had to treble in size above that of the great
apes.

2. This brain development had to come *after* the child was
born, in the baby's first year. If it came in the womb, the child
could not be born at all.

3. Childhood had to be lengthened, to allow the human
young to learn enough habits to deal successfully with their
environment at maturity.

4. Family bonds had to survive seasonal mating and become
permanent "if this odd new creature was to be prepared for
his adult role."

Thus we lost the hairy covering of proto-men, our jaws
and teeth were reduced in size, our brows were shortened,
our chins built up, the period of childhood greatly lengthened
and a biological basis for monogamy established.

It would be fascinating to know when and where true
man first walked on earth. Did he arise in several localities?
Most probably not, though some of us who live in the New
World cannot help wondering whether man, like the civilizations of Peru and Mexico, may not have been indigenous
here. We admit that Stone Age bands from the Old World
crossed into Alaska; we admit that Polynesian canoes may
have landed on the west coast of South America. But it
would give us a kind of New World pleasure if archaeologists
should dig up unimpeachable evidence of *Homo Ameri-*

---

[1] Following Loren Eiseley: *The Immense Journey* (Random House, 1957).

canus, standing erect and speaking, 100,000 years ago. The probabilities, however, are all against it.

THE RACES OF MAN

No two human beings have the same complement of genes, except identical twins who come from a single cell. A "pure" race never existed, nor can possibly exist; Hitler's "Aryan race" was pure anti-knowledge.

Members of the same species in differing environments become genetically different through natural selection, if they live apart long enough. *This is what a geneticist means when he speaks of races.*[2] "Races" are groups within a species which differ in the frequency of certain genes. If the environments differ greatly—say a tropical sun versus Northern snows—the genetic difference will become marked. In the case of man, the group which lived in Africa selected out the genes which increase the amount of melanin in the skin, turning it brown or black as protection against the sun. The North European branches developed genes producing blond hair and blue eyes. But some blue eyes continued in Africa, and some dark skins in the North.

If two races are separated long enough, natural selection will transform one of them into a new species, incapable of breeding with the other. Despite his migrations and global separation, this has not happened in the case of man; the species, so far as we know, has never split. Races have evolved with differing skin color, hair texture, heights, weights, lips, noses, eye folds, but the power to interbreed has not been lost.

Scientists explain this strange phenomenon by pointing to a double migration, unique to man. Homo sapiens, they tell us, journeyed off to the ends of the earth, and then journeyed back again—at least some bands journeyed back. Certain groups were cut off, as in Australia; but twenty thousand years of isolation in Australia was not long enough to evolve

---

2 Following T. Dobzhansky in *Scientific American Reader*.

a new species; bushmen and whites can interbreed. This coming and going of human bands over most of the habitable globe provided a thorough mixture of genes, and effectively prevented racial purity. We are a mongrel lot.

Unrestricted breeding does not mean, as some people suppose, that descendants will ultimately conform to a single type. The stock of human genes is so large that diversity will continue large. The so-called pool of human genes at the present time is something in the order of 100 trillion—2.5 billion living persons, times 20,000 pairs of genes each.[3]

IS THERE A SUPERIOR RACE?

Did diverse conditions cause certain races to develop greater intelligence? We have no evidence of that. Mental differences between the races have not been proved. Says Stern: "A normal man's genetic equipment provides him with a wide potential of mental performance, from very low to very high. As with a rubber balloon, the state of expansion of his mind at any given time is hardly a measure of its expandability."

Differences between individuals of the same race are far more significant than the highly problematical differences between races. The effects of environment and training on individuals are so great that genetic differences are often masked. Eskimos can be taught to fly a Constellation; the children of primitive forest folk have earned degrees at Oxford.

The really big news about human intelligence is how sparingly all races use their excellent mental equipment. The really big question is how natural selection produced an instrument with a power considerably beyond its normal use. The words of Alfred Russel Wallace come back to haunt us: "We may safely infer that the savage possesses a brain capable, if cultivated and developed, of performing work of a kind and degree far beyond what he ever requires to do."

---

[3] Calculation from Curt Stern in *Scientific American Reader*.

In all the vast panorama of life there is probably no more puzzling query than this.

THE ENCHANTED LOOM

Sir Charles Sherrington, the great eye specialist, had a gift for a striking phrase. He called the human brain "the enchanted loom"; elsewhere he called it "the great ravelled knot." Alfred Korzybski, when asked to distinguish between men and other creatures, used to growl in his rich Polish accent, "A quarter of an inch of cortex."

Specialists tell us—perhaps with a touch of poetry—that if an electronic computer were built to match the nerve connections of the brain, it would require a skyscraper to house it, the power of Niagara Falls to run it, and all the water of Niagara to cool it. Natural selection has produced an astronomical number of patterns since the original cell in the prehistoric sea, but none to compare in subtlety and power with this instrument.

The cortex, or roof brain, is the distinctive human organ. In Homo sapiens, more than 75 per cent [4] of the cortex is occupied by "association areas," which relate new information coming in to past experience, and so prepare the individual to make a choice and act. The brain of that intelligent mammal, the rat, by way of contrast, is mostly devoted to areas which give him information about the immediate environment, but permit no such comparison with the past, no such weighing of alternatives.

Electronic computers are now constructed with built-in memories, such as magnetic revolving drums, batteries of cathode-ray tubes, reels of magnetic tape. No one yet knows how human memories are stored, nor how much of past experience is permanently filed. In seventy years of living, a person can theoretically receive fifteen trillion separate "bits" of information, a "bit" being the smallest unit of an

---

[4] Following George W. Gray in *Scientific American Reader*.

incoming message, as worked out by communication engineers.

THE GREAT ENIGMA

Natural selection, as observed in other forms of life, does not explain the brain and its memory mechanism. The enigma pointed out by Wallace grows in importance: Why did the human mind develop beyond the primitive needs of its possessor? Wallace lived among "savages" in Malaya, studied their language, and was amazed and puzzled by its intricacy and precision. He knew from firsthand experience what he was talking about when he raised his query, but he was brushed aside by the savants of his era. Anthropologists and biologists today are veering to his support.

Various theories have been advanced to explain the growth of the brain, and perhaps the one that stands up best is *language*. "With every advance in language, in symbolic thought," Eiseley speculates, "the brain paths multiplied." This does not explain the apparent excess capacity of the brain, but it does account for the equivalent latent intelligence of all human races. Children everywhere have had to learn a complicated language structure, causing Benjamin Lee Whorf to remind us that "the crudest savage may unconsciously manipulate with effortless ease a linguistic system so intricate, manifoldly systematized, and intellectually difficult, that it requires the life-time study of our greatest scholars to describe its workings."

We take spoken language, especially our own, so much for granted that we lose all sense of what a profound intellectual achievement it represents in every individual. All the races—black, yellow and white; "savage," "barbarous" and "civilized"—have without exception been put through this unique and exacting discipline.

THE MISSING LINK

Alfred Russel Wallace was brushed aside because the Darwinian school of evolution had developed a tidy, logical, straight-line theory of descent. Darwin believed, for instance, that the skill with which an Eskimo handled a canoe was inherited, not learned after birth—thus putting the Eskimo a few rungs down the ladder of intelligence. He believed that the intelligence of Andaman Islanders was only a little above that of the chimpanzee. His school was convinced that the Hottentot language of Africa was close to chattering of monkeys.

The straight Darwinian line supposedly proceeded from monkeys to the higher apes, to the lowest savages, higher nature peoples (say the Eskimos), to barbarians of various shades, and finally to a Victorian papa, magnificent in frock coat and side whiskers, the apex of evolution. Somewhere along the line between apes and Hottentots was a "missing link" which, when found, would verify and complete the whole sequence. Archaeologists dug furiously in pursuit of this character. I was brought up to expect his discovery at any time, and one fears that many educated people are still expecting it today.

Meanwhile a practical joker in 1914 cemented the jaw of an orangutan upon a human skull, and buried it for archaeologists to find near Piltdown, England. The fraud was widely believed to be the missing link. For forty years, until X-ray analysis revealed the hoax, "Piltdown man" confused and retarded the true story of human descent.

The true story, or at least the one most widely accepted today, is the one recited in this chapter, beginning with the common ancestor of perhaps twenty million years ago. There was no missing link, and the Victorian papa, for all his sartorial magnificence, had no better apparatus in his skull than Hottentot, Eskimo or Hopi. He had a far better education, with all the vast accumulation of Western culture to draw upon. The Darwinians never grasped the significance of *culture* in human development. Their straight-line theory has gone with the antimacassar, the bustle, and the great Piltdown hoax.

THE UNIQUENESS OF MAN

Homo sapiens is not in command at the center of the universe, as the Greeks believed, but it is fair to call him the highest form of life to date, the most unique and interesting outcome of two billion years of natural selection.

As we have seen, he came late on the stage. His remote ancestors first freed their hands by walking upright, and gradually adjusted to a harsh environment by using their power to reason, lodged in an ever more complex nervous system and brain. Without language, abstract thought was impossible, and speech centers and language may have evolved together. It is not unreasonable to assume that proto-man did not become true man until he could talk.

The roof brain, language, abstract thought are responsible for the development of culture, a phenomenon found nowhere else in nature. It is a phenomenon now so powerful that it seems to be displacing natural selection. Many scientists believe that there has been no substantial change in man's bodily or mental equipment for fifty thousand years —except possibly downward. Instead of modifying hand or ear or skin to meet new conditions, we develop new tools, textiles, food supply, trade routes, forms of organization. A new skin covering would be transmitted through the genes; the new tools are purely cultural, their use learned after birth.

Later chapters will be devoted to the culture concept with its tremendous implications. Without an understanding of the culture concept, most of our modern problems—war, poverty, population pressures, conservation—are insoluble. No child is ever born with the remotest trace of cultural behavior. He has the machinery for speech but no words, no instinctive customs, or beliefs, no moral standards. He learns by observation and example, and is deliberately taught by the elders and peers of his society.

Einstein refined the physics of Newton and displaced absolute Time and absolute Space with the principles of relativity. The time is ripe for an Einstein in the life sciences to refine the natural selection of Darwin, and better account for a brain which can do more than it is normally required to do. The puzzle, however, encourages an idea which should not be lost on generalists. If we could manage to use our minds nearer to their capacity, we might attack the problems of our age with more confidence and success.

7 . Hunters

IN 1800, when Napoleon was on the march, the prehistory of man was quite unknown. Behind the written records, which began only about fifty-five hundred years ago, lay a deep void, partly filled with myths. Some of the myths were poetic and charming, like the tales of the Golden Age to which the Greeks and other ancient peoples looked back, or like the first chapter of Genesis.

Most of the great historians wrote their books while this void existed, with the result that "history" came to mean only the period covered by the written documents. When a person said "history teaches," or "the implacable judgment of history," he was referring to the last fifty-five hundred years, the brief tail end of the story of mankind. The written records, furthermore, beginning with account books in Sumerian temples, leave a good deal to be desired in the way of accuracy. The idea of objective research was almost unknown and myth and fact were often intermingled.

UNWRITTEN HISTORY

Today, a significant change has come over the study of the distant past. In some respects the techniques of scientists who compile unwritten history produce more reliable information than the documents of the accredited historians. Archaeologists and anthropologists can cross-check dates and events with an accuracy often beyond library scholars.

64

Geoffrey Bibby observes that with small exceptions we now know what has happened in Europe since the first man entered the continent.[1] Archaeologists have told us when major changes occurred and why, who brought innovations and from where. With this European achievement behind them, they can now launch out into Asia, Africa, the Americas, armed with similar techniques of digging, dating, comparing. "The archaeologist," says Gordon R. Willey, "deals with broken pieces of something which once was vital and whole, and searches for the patterns into which the pieces fit."

Archaeologists used to ask: when did the "battle-ax people" enter Europe? (Answer: around four thousand years ago.) Today such a question has split into at least three: (1) How many battle-ax people? (2) How thickly did they occupy? (3) How far did they intermarry with earlier inhabitants?

The archaeologist is now deep in density curves, laboratory and statistical analysis for events that occurred long before a spoken word was ever written down. He asks: What kinds of creatures did the early hunters kill for food? How did they kill and prepare them? People could survive for thousands of years without writing, but not many days without eating. The archaeologist is also paying more attention to individual members of the band. He wonders, for instance, about the bowls of food in a child's tomb, and how those who mourned may have felt.

Unwritten history spans a period many times longer than that of documented history, and no inquiring mind can study the clues to this story without being fascinated and excited. How much of it is significant for the generalist, and why?

THE LESSON OF UNWRITTEN HISTORY

A reader can easily be overwhelmed in trying to trace the

---

[1] *The Testimony of the Spade* (Knopf, 1956). I shall draw from this important survey throughout the present chapter.

endless migrations of prehistory, to distinguish the differing shapes of flints and pottery, in trying to understand the mysteries of Stonehenge. He can take sides as to whether Neanderthal man became extinct or was incorporated with the Cro-Magnons. He can spend many hours admiring those excellently executed, and excellently publicized, paintings of bison and deer in the caves of France and Spain. But in doing so he can lose sight of certain broader considerations.

Unwritten history helps us establish a kinship with ancient peoples as they solve their arduous problems of getting a living and coming to terms with their environment. We see them flaking a chunk of flint instead of running a turret lathe, inventing a bow instead of an outboard motor, bartering copper axes instead of tending store. We see them trying to keep warm in a polar climate, experimenting with color and design, developing a spoken language and teaching it to the children. Unwritten history ties man into nature, close to the moving ice and to the beasts and vegetation that followed the ice. We draw from it a long perspective on where we belong in the scheme of things and how brief is the time we call "civilization."

Professor Gordon Childe of London University, whom Bibby quotes, expresses the point.

> Progress is an indivisible whole in which the invention of a new way of hafting an axe formed a necessary prelude to the invention of the steam-engine or the aeroplane. In the first innovations the germs of all subsequent improvements were latent; and the first steps on the path of discovery were the hardest. Thus the achievements of our nameless forerunners are in a real sense present in our cultural heritage today.

A NICE AIRY CAVE

When Dr. Carleton Coon goes digging in the Near East, he first of all makes friends with the local people and hires some of them to help him dig.[2] Then he looks up at

---

[2] Carleton S. Coon: *The Seven Caves* (Knopf, 1957).

a likely hillside and muses: "If I were my great-great . . . grandfather what would I look for in a nice cave?" The water supply is important, so is a good view over the game area, and protection against cave bears. Time and again such imaginative reconnoitering has led Dr. Coon to a profitable site. I like to stand there with him on a hillside ten thousand years ago.

Having located the cave, he asks again how people would use it. Any sensible man, he concludes, would spend his cave-dwelling time about twenty meters from the back, and ten meters from the south edge. That is where he would find the best compromise between light and shelter.

Unwritten history, as revealed by men like Coon, soon corrects the stereotype of the "cave man," brandishing a knotted club in one hand and clutching the hair of a captive female in the other. Our ancestors did not live in caves if they could help it; caves then as now were dank, dark, and full of smoke that made one's eyes smart. Even if people liked them, there were not nearly enough caves to go around.

A co-operative family—usually monogamous, as we have noted—was essential to survival, and dragging in captive females by the hair does nothing to keep peace in the family. One would not go so far as to speculate that father ever washed up the pots after a meal of boiled reindeer, but surely he must have helped bring up the children and teach the boys to hunt.

Coon explains that while our ancestors preferred camps in open country, they were forced into caves from time to time, especially in winter. And in a dry cave, of course, the historical evidence is best preserved. Much larger areas where people lived in the open have been leveled and pulverized by ice sheets, leaving few artifacts or bones to tell a story. There is some unwritten history to be found in glacial drifts, some in summer hunting camps along the Baltic with their huge "kitchen middens," and some preserved in bogs and swamps.

CASPIAN CAVE

Caves, however, remain the best source for data. Let us inspect one which Coon found on the shore of the Caspian Sea in 1951. Its floor went down like a five-pound candy box, layer after layer. It required careful engineering to keep the layers distinct, and leave an undisturbed cross section for other scientists to check. The rock bottom was down so many feet that the work had to be shored against dangerous cave-ins. Eight layers were unearthed:

	Carbon-14 date
Islamic culture on top	A.D. 730
Parthian layer	B.C. 250
Early Iron Age people	B.C. 735
Painted-pottery tenants	B.C. 2880
Soft-ware Neolithic people	B.C. 4435
Sub-Neolithic people	B.C. 6120
Vole eaters (plenty of bones from these tiny mouselike creatures)	B.C. 7240
Seal hunters (near rock bottom)	B.C. 9910

Thus below the layer of goat dung that covers the floor of most caves in the Near East, sandwiched in between the rubble, sand, red earth, black earth and bedrock, was a clear record of eight different cultures, covering a total period of almost eleven thousand years.

From each layer Coon took a sample of what was once living matter—a bone, a piece of wood or charcoal, a textile fragment—and sent it to an American laboratory for dating based on its amount of carbon 14, the latest and best method. Before this invention, archaeologists used the less accurate dating methods of (1) analyzing layers of sediment; (2) microscopic study of fossil pollen; (3) cross reference via similar artifacts to cultures already dated.

Every living thing contains some carbon 14, a radioactive isotope with a half life of 5,568 years. A tree cut down 5,568 years ago, or charcoal from that tree, will produce half as many clicks on a Geiger counter as a tree cut yesterday, and so on back by a sliding scale. With specimens in hand, experts can now calculate dates many thousands of years in the past within a small margin of error.[3]

What did Coon find in his eight layers; what do archaeologists generally look for? They sift the dirt for broken pottery, the charred remains of cooking fires, animal bones telling what was cooked and eaten (our ancestors were as careless of their discarded bones as modern motorists are careless of their beer cans), hand axes, knives, harpoons, arrows, cores and shivers of flint, pieces of textile, bone needles, beads, matting. *Especially and particularly they look for human bones.* A skull, even a fragment of a skull, is a great prize, and fills the digger with feverish excitement.

Whole histories can be constructed from flint alone. Flint scraps tell the specialist what kind of tools were made even if no tools are found. Flints are works of art as well as tools, and the digger studies and admires them, as other collectors might study Venetian glass. The original flint stones range in size from an apple to a watermelon, and the manufactured products vary from a simple cutting edge to a sophisticated Egyptian knife, hard as a dagger of Florentine steel, and as graceful. Some bushmen in Australia are working flint today—almost the last of the Stone Age craftsmen to do so.

DIGS IN AMERICA AND CHINA

The caves of Western Europe helped to upset the chronology of Bishop Ussher, and in Europe the complicated techniques of a proper "dig" were developed during the last hundred years. Now they are being put to use in Russia, Siberia, the Middle East, India, China, Africa and North America. Very little is reported as yet from South America. The diggers are fitting the pieces together and finding answers to many important questions, including

---

3 It has been reported that H-bomb explosions in the Pacific upset carbon-14 dating tests in laboratories as far away as Philadelphia. Samples had to be sent to New Zealand, where fall-out was less.

this one: Did Stone Age cultures, cut off from one another, tend to develop a similar pattern?

In North America, dated charcoal remains show that Stone Age hunters cooked game beside a stream in Nevada some twenty-four thousand years ago. Today the region is desert. With the charcoal were found the bones of a large American camel, a long-horned bison, two species of wild horse, and an awl made from the camel's leg bones. The date means that hunters from Asia crossed Bering Strait a good deal earlier than had been supposed.

Digging in Tamaulipas, Mexico, in 1954, archaeologists excavated a cave with seven culture layers, including tools, weapons, mats, rope, foodstuffs. In the fourth layer they found the corncobs of an early form of maize. In the fifth layer were arrows, tobacco and chili.

Western scientists began digging in China in the 1920's, and presently Chinese archaeologists joined them. They unearthed a character whom they called Sinanthropus, who lived some 500,000 years ago—a dawn man, like the 80-pound ape man unearthed by Dr. R. A. Dart in South Africa. Near Sinanthropus was a stone chopper he might have made.

In the deep layers of one Chinese cave, diggers found stone tools, perforated beads of stone, and bone needles. Higher up in the same cave, they found bones of sheep, ox, horse, indicating that the tenants had learned to domesticate animals. The cultural development of China as well as North America parallels that of Mesopotamia and India. Stone Age peoples, with no contact with one another, do indeed tend to follow a similar development in their artifacts and inventions. Why not? Mankind is one species.

TIMETABLE

Specialists divide unwritten history in many ways. In almost any text we find such terms as "diluvial," "pre-Chellian," "Middle Clactonian," "Early Levalloisian," "Acheulean," "Mousterian," "Solutrean," "Magdalenian."

The names often stand for the villages where bones were found, or for the digger who found them. They are doubtless helpful for specialists, but hard on generalists. Some day the nomenclature may be reordered and simplified. For the generalist, the following sequence should be adequate:

1. *Old Stone Age or Paleolithic era.* It may run back to the advent of true man, 200,000 to 300,000 years ago. Bands of nomadic hunters pursued the game across the African veldt. In the north they killed mammoth, woolly rhinoceros, musk ox, bison, elk, reindeer, in forest and steppe in Europe, Asia and finally North America.

2. *New Stone Age or Neolithic era.* Beginning perhaps 10,000 years ago, but varying with location—earlier in the Middle East, later in India, Europe, China, North America. Skilled hunters with finely wrought flints, pursued modern types of game in modern types of forest. They begin the domestication of animals—the first experiments in agriculture.

3. *The Bronze Age.* First metalworking, in tin, copper, and alloys. Agriculture and irrigation developing. First towns. Achilles and Hector fought with bronze swords beneath the walls of Homer's Troy.

4. *The Iron Age.* Civilization in full swing.

The ages of Bronze and Iron we will consider in later chapters. In this chapter we work in stone.

SOUTH OF THE ICE

Homo sapiens was in a sense the product of the moving ice, retreating as the glaciers waxed, advancing as they waned. Vegetation was governed by the ice, game followed the vegetation, and man followed the game. Three zones of climate formed along the ice sheet. On its edge came a belt of soggy ground, perhaps fifty miles wide, like the muskeg of Alaska today. Mosses and dwarf willows were the only vegetation. Then came a belt of windblown steppe, perhaps one hundred miles wide, whose cover of grass fed herds of wild horses and other grazing animals. They could be hunted by men able to live through the winter. South of the steppe belt was the boreal forest, much like the north woods of Canada and Scandinavia today—a land of lakes and pointed firs. As the ice retreated, these three zones moved north with it.

Hunters followed their favored meat supply, surviving in winter by living in a cave if they could find one, and by fashioning suits of fur and skins, like Eskimos today. They cleaned the skins with scrapers and sewed them with needles of flint and bone. Tents were also made of skins. Siberian tribes using such tents in recent times have survived cold down to −75° F. Proto-man may well have been a vegetarian, like his cousins the great apes, but when we first encounter true man he has become hunter and meat eater. He roasted his dinner in a carefully preserved fire. Human teeth are not those of a carnivorous animal, but the dietary change was made a long time ago.

It took a lot of organization for a creature without a furry hide to keep warm, and more organization to fill the larder. For evidence, consider the great heaps of mammoth bones discovered near Leipzig. The huge beasts were killed by Stone Age hunters on a narrow game trail between the edges of the Scandinavian and the Alpine ice sheets. Teamwork, a good communication system and careful advance planning were needed to trap and slay these hairy, eight-ton monsters armed with ten-foot tusks. The big brain, language and group discipline were all in action there in the gorge between the glaciers. We can almost hear the hoarse shouts of triumph when the mammoth was overcome.

Bone heaps suggest that hunters specialized on certain animals—mammoth, reindeer, or wild horse. They killed them selectively, choosing individuals of specified age and sex—as in the Chicago stockyards. This specialization, says Bibby, required much training and yielded the rich reward of a dependable food supply. One wonders how the food was preserved—by smoking it, perhaps? In winter it may have lasted for months; in summer not so long. The first civilizations depended on a storable grain, but Stone Age hunters apparently solved the problem of a storable meat. Most hunting animals, in contrast, kill for the day alone.

The mammoth became rare as the ice retreated, and men began to hunt reindeer on the steppes. Later, when the forests closed in, the game changed from reindeer to elk, red deer and aurochs.

> It was no mean thing to achieve self-sufficiency in the marginal lands on the rim of the ice; to learn how to convert the only two things the hunting-grounds provided, reindeer and flint, into tools and weapons and clothes and food and shelter, and even have a little surplus . . . for personal adornment and artistic expression. But the price was conservatism. . . .

The generalist pricks up his ears at the word "surplus." Here, on the rim of the ice, twenty thousand years and more ago, is the central proposition in economics. Civilization, architecture, art, philosophy are impossible until the tribe stores enough food to allow time for activities other than food getting. Then comes the acute problem of how to divide the surplus among the members of the tribe—and politics enters.

A man can make a harpoon from the antlers of a reindeer to kill another reindeer. But the antlers of red deer are too soft, and techniques of harpoon making must be revolutionized. Perhaps the reindeer hunters, like the Bourbons of France, were unable to change their habits. We do not know. Perhaps they followed the reindeer north, while a new people moved in to hunt the red deer in the deepening forest. Technological change sometimes became a major problem for our ancestors, as it is for ourselves.

One hunting clan pressed up behind the ice to the Siberian arctic, where they changed their habits sufficiently to learn to fish from kayaks, and ultimately to become Eskimos. Eskimos apparently did not cross into Alaska until about three thousand years ago, long after other Stone Age peoples had crossed the strait to continue hunting elk and deer in the forests of North America.

As the last ice sheet retreated, the hunters of Iraq, Iran and Afghanistan had tamed the dog and developed the bow. They were working wood as well as flint. The climate was less arid than now, for goats had not eaten off the vegetation to produce deserts. Lakes and streams offered hunters a rich bag of fish and wild fowl to supplement bigger game. It was an era of relative prosperity, with the food supply well ahead of population. Coon believes that people in the Middle East had a far better living then than now.

A NOTE ON DIFFUSION

We have noted the constant migrations which, through interbreeding, kept our ancestors one species. As bands moved back and forth they picked up new inventions from one another—a process the specialists call "diffusion." The unwritten history of the New World reveals considerable diffusion from the Old World, but always in the inventions and artifacts of the Stone Age. Harpoons and skinning knives in Greenland are similar to those unearthed in Norway. The bow, skin boats, hollow-ground stone adzes, are found in both New England and Northern Europe. "Comb" pottery spread from China to Virginia and Tennessee. Rock carvings of animals—apparently anatomical charts for hunters, to judge by the telltale "life line" engraved from mouth to heart—are found in Northern Asia, around Lake Superior, and in Arizona, as well as in the Pyrenees. It is a long journey on foot, via Bering Strait, from a cave in Spain to one in New Mexico, but "the culture forms of both," says Bibby, "are built up from the same foundation, which must lie in ancient Asiatic stone age culture." [4]

THOSE CAVE ARTISTS

Our ancestors of the last ice age had high foreheads and big brain cases. Some tribes averaged taller and stronger,

---

[4] More digging in South Africa may displace Asia as the cradle of the race.

judging by the skeletons, than modern Europeans. In the caves of France and Spain they proved themselves gifted artists as well as skilled craftsmen and mighty hunters. Generalists know about the cave sculpture and frescoes of the ancestor called Cro-Magnon man, and have seen reproductions of his spirited work.

Not all of us know, however, the *reason* for this artistry. A moment's thought makes it clear that a pitch-dark cave, which often must be entered by crawling on one's hands and knees, does not provide an adequate art gallery. The figures must have been painted most arduously by the glare of a primitive torch. It is now generally agreed that the paintings were partly an exercise in symbolic magic. By representing the animal in this sacred place, often etching the "life line" from mouth to heart, the artist sought to enhance the fortunes of the hunt. A rough analogy today might be the symbolic blessing of fishermen's nets.

These works were done by superb artists, possibly a guild traveling from cave to cave, some fifteen thousand years ago. Whenever Homo sapiens gains a little on his food supply, he turns to art—etching decorations on deer antlers, designing borders for cooking pots, engraving weapons and tools, bringing color and composition into the work of his hands. In Mexico I have visited villages where nearly every person was an artist.

ERAS OF PEACE

Unwritten history discloses generations of pacifists, as well as artists. For long periods, the cave layers will show only tools for hunting and domestic uses, with no swords, daggers or spears for fighting.

War can hardly be a universal human inheritance, if strong men can go for centuries without indulging in it. War comes with food shortages, with rivalries among heads of organized states, with the institution of nationalism. The people of Switzerland and Sweden have not gone to war for a century, and anthropologists find remote tribes which never go to war.[5] The generalist makes a cardinal distinction between a tendency to personal violence, native in the genes, and organized warfare, which obviously is not.

NEANDERTHAL PEOPLE

Bones found in the village of Neanderthal, Germany, showed a race far more primitive in appearance than the hunters we have been discussing. Similar bones and skulls were later unearthed in France and North Africa. Evidence from the cave layers indicates the Neanderthal people lived at the same time as the Cro-Magnon people. Coon, who has dug up the former, and come rather to like them, says that their tools were not inferior, and their brains about as large. The best theory (1957), he says, is that the Neanderthal people descended from proto-men, evolved into a separate species, and finally became extinct.

Everything set forth in this story of Stone Age hunters depends on the diggers of cave, bog and glacial drift, on their reasoning and their laboratory work. The history which specialists have pieced together without benefit of written documents holds us spellbound and throws long shafts of light into the future, as well as into the past. "They dig in pity and humility, that the dead may live again."

If we assume, with most students, that the men of fifty thousand years ago were as intelligent as men today, and that civilization has been known only for about fifty-five hundred years, it is likely that the children who are born today are better equipped, *by inheritance*, for the roving life of hunting bands than for living in cities. They are born equipped, if you like, to deal in the open with mammoths and saber-toothed tigers, with sudden dangers and emergencies, equipped to survive without regular meals, indeed with no assurance where the next meal is coming from. The "soft generation" of young men who were taken from schools

---

[5] Such as the Eskimo, also the Arapesh of New Guinea, described by Margaret Mead.

and offices in 1940 and sent to fight around the globe in the arctic and the jungle, were able to adjust to terrible hardships, thanks to this native equipment.

I am not referring to that supposed "primitive savage in all of us," stupid in mentality and ferocious in his desires. To find this hairy character would take us back to proto-man, say another 500,000 years. No, I am thinking of the built-in equipment for acceleration in emergencies—built-in because men who lacked it failed to survive—equipment ready to trigger off a massive reaction through the glandular structures and blood-chemical responses, and thus save our lives. I am thinking of the potential strength to stand cold and hunger and sleeplessness, bear children unaided, pack up and travel afoot for long distances and many days.

Whatever Utopias the planners may be planning for us should allow for these deep-seated characteristics of our human inheritance. They should include plenty of open country, and some room for living dangerously.

8 . Farmers

ECONOMICS has been described as an attempt to make sure of one's dinner. Stone Age men had to keep hunting pretty steadily if the family were to eat. A butchered mammoth might provide a little surplus, and allow time for etching aurochs or speculating about the unknown; but mostly one had to keep on the game trail. We can reasonably assume that a more dependable food supply —or dependable economy—was a prime goal of neolithic hunters.

The goal, whether conscious or not, was achieved by means of two inventions in places as widely separated as Mesopotamia and Peru. Once these inventions were adopted, the economy of our ancestors underwent a profound and unprecedented change.

The first invention was the domestication of certain animals.

The second, and even more important, was the conversion of wild plants into storable grain.

Thus a surplus of food could be accumulated, and the pressure of continuous hunting be relaxed. The time gained allowed the big brain and the manipulating hand more opportunity to experiment, contrive and build. Settled villages, then towns, cities, organized priesthoods, policemen, civilization, became inevitable.

In Mesopotamia, animals were domesticated before grain was cultivated; in Egypt it was the other way around. The Nile, with its annual flood-borne deposit of fertile soil, encouraged agricultural experiments in advance of animal breeding.

Hunting bands had domesticated the dog and invented the bow and arrow. The theory is that fox or wolf cubs were reared with the band and taught to aid in the hunt. The cubs learned that it was easier to get their food in company with a huntsman, and gradually evolved into a tamer species. Early cave drawings show dogs bringing in game. By the time of the first cities, several breeds had been developed— a slender greyhound type, a short-legged terrier type—while in some areas dogs were raised for food.

Success in domesticating the dog may have given some Stone Age Darwin the idea of experimenting with wild sheep and wild goats. The experiments were certainly made, and presently extended to wild camels, pigs, and cattle. In the Americas wild turkeys were early domesticated. Thus in favored locations hunters assisted their hunting with dogs, and supplemented their diet of game with home-grown meat, together with fresh milk and cheese. Domestic animals also provided wool and hides for clothing. The hunter became part-time herdsman, a change which tended to slow his migrations and hold him in more permanent camps and settlements.

WHEAT, RICE AND MAIZE

Plants and wild grasses had long been gathered, possibly in the unconscious craving for a balanced diet. Raw meat supplies vitamins, but cooked meat often does not. Indians of the high plateau in Mexico for thousands of years supplemented their regular diet of cooked beans and maize with pulque, a strong beer brewed from the century plant and rich in vitamins. When the Mexican government in the 1920's outlawed pulque in the interest of temperance, plateau Indians began to sicken in such alarming numbers that its use had to be restored, pending adequate vitamin substitutes.

Herdsmen of Mesopotamia, when a food surplus gave them a little leisure, began to experiment with plants, selecting and tending them in hope of greater yield. The actual steps to ordered tillage remain unknown, but the end product, and the logic of the drive to that end, are clear enough. Wheat as developed in Mesopotamia was probably the first dependable grain crop known to man. Then came wheat in Egypt, wheat in India, rice in China, and maize in the Western Hemisphere. Mesopotamia, Egypt and India may have developed wheat independently.

The harvested crop could be stored in granaries made of mud bricks or wood. Failing serious drought, all the people of the tribe could be assured of regular meals; their economic problem was solved. Man-hours formerly spent on long hunting journeys now went to settled tillage, though some hunting continued.

A profound economic revolution was under way, far greater than the industrial revolution of the mid-1800's, or the electronic revolution of the mid-1900's. A hunting culture could never have produced Babylon and Memphis, nor could a culture depending solely upon domestic animals. These cities, any city, can be built only on a grain economy.

TECHNIQUES

Wild ancestors of both wheat and barley still grow in the Near East, and a Luther Burbank could repeat the process of converting them to storable grain—though it might take several generations of Burbanks. In the forested areas, trees were felled with broad axes made of polished flint, axes so efficient that archaeologists experimenting with these ancient tools have cut down an eight-inch tree in eight minutes. The slash was then burned off, much as Mexican Indians burn the bush today to make a milpa, and seed grain was sown in the ashes with a stick. Such cropping soon exhausts the soil, and the first farmers repeated the operation in another patch of virgin forest. Farmers in Mesopotamia after a time improved on this wasteful cycle by inventing irrigation and terracing.

In Egypt there were few trees and no bush to burn, and techniques were very different. The Nile took care of soil preparation by laying down a new deposit every summer. The soft mud spread inland for miles, and was worked with wooden hoes and plows. Sheep trod in flax seed, as well as wheat and barley. The crop was harvested with curved flint sickles, then threshed by donkeys, winnowed by women, and stored in beehive-shaped silos. The Nile is still unwearying in its fertility, and the *fellahin* today make a crop not too differently from their ancestors of seven thousand years ago.

In China, the neolithic era arrived later than in the Near East, and there is no evidence of early diffusion between the two. Chinese hunters in due course domesticated the sheep, ox and horse. Then quite suddenly, about four thousand years ago the sparsely settled land began to teem with life. Thousands of villages appeared in the river valleys, lined with terraces planted to rice. In addition to grain farmers and stock raisers, there were skilled carpenters, weavers, pottery makers. Thus China, quite independently, followed the sequence of Mesopotamia—hunter to herdsman to settled farmer.

THE SPREAD OF AGRICULTURE

Husbandry, as we have seen, was invented in the Middle East, about seven thousand years ago. Whether techniques were exchanged between Mesopotamia and Egypt in very early times we do not know. As the centuries went by, the art of tillage spread into Europe by two well-established routes; from Iraq via Turkey and the Black Sea into the Danube country; from Egypt via the North African coast and across the Mediterranean into Spain and France. Did it spread into India from the Middle East, or was agriculture developed there independently? More digs by archaeologists are needed to answer this question. Rice was certainly invented independently in China. Maize was certainly invented independently in the New World; indeed Mexico and Peru may even have developed maize independently of each other.

Here then is the cause of the greatest social and economic revolution known to man—storable grain in Mesopotamia, in Egypt, India, China, Mexico, Peru. Three of the centers were certainly developed independently; all six may have been. All demonstrate clearly a common human need for a dependable food supply. Their creators can, of course, have felt no need to establish civilization, something beyond all imagining. But in the wake of the food surplus, towns and cities, architects and builders, firemen and water pipes, theaters, temples and newspapers, cops and robbers, had to come.

FARMERS IN EUROPE

Farmers entered Europe by two routes as noted, about five thousand years ago, two thousand years after the first wheat was waving along the Euphrates. The native hunters of Europe apparently invented no husbandry at all; they were the backward peoples of the time, the "lesser breeds without the law." It took some five hundred years for agriculture to spread throughout the continent. One is reminded of the pioneers of North America, whose descendants spent nearly four hundred years overrunning that continent, from the landing of Cortes at Veracruz in 1521 to the closing of the American frontier in 1890.

When archaeologists uncovered the ruins of villages built on wooden piles in Swiss lakes, they found evidence of domestic animals, of wheat, bread baking, woven textiles, the shaping of heavy timbers, and polished flint tools—all far beyond the arts of native European hunters. The scientists soundly concluded that the lake villagers must have been invaders from the Middle East. Tillage was not so much an art diffused to European hunters, as the result of the hunters being driven out by invaders from another continent.

The "kitchen-midden" people of Denmark give us a fascinating case of cultural lag. They were hunters and most untidy in their housekeeping. They threw bones and shells and broken shards all around their camps, in piles like the culm bank of a modern mine—hence the name "kitchen midden," or in plain terms, garbage dumps. They apparently did not fight the invading farmers from the East, but they would have no part of the newfangled methods—burning the forest and frightening the game indeed! The kitchen-midden folk continued to hunt, or try to hunt, for many decades, with farmers growing crops all around them. When finally they capitulated to progress, they accepted its products in this order: (1) pigs, (2) cows, (3) wheat, (4) beer. The effects of the beer, one suspects, were less serious than the effects of trade whisky on the Indians of North America.

It took about five hundred years to exhaust the virgin soil of Europe by the felling and burning method. Before the end, however, while land was still plentiful and homesteads were to be had for the labor of clearing, Europe enjoyed a long period of prosperity and peace—another instance of the fact that war is not instinctive. Then the "battle-ax" people from the Eastern steppes descended on the happy and peaceful farmers and appropriated their holdings. Archaeologists follow the invasion of these tough characters by digging up their special type of polished battle-ax.

When tillage spread to the British Isles, the demand for tools mounted, especially flints to cut down the forest. Four centers for manufacturing stones axes have been identified —in the Lake District, in Scotland, Wales and North Ireland. These centers we may be sure did not practice mass production, but may well have originated the factory system, some three thousand years ago.

Meanwhile, amid the vast monoliths of Stonehenge in England, specialists piece together the evidence of an early system of religion. The massive architecture of Stonehenge was oriented to the equinox, and religious ceremonies celebrating the sun god were carried on there by a trading peo-

ple, originally from North Africa, who had learned how to
work in bronze.

THE STORY OF MAIZE

Europeans call wheat "corn," Americans call maize "corn";
for each it is the staff of life. It would be interesting to track
down all the early grains, but a brief review of one of them
is all we have space for. As an American I am particularly
interested in maize.

Europeans and Asians do not seem to have been so emotionally involved with their "corn" as American Indians.
How maize originated is a mystery, as no single wild grass
is known from which it could have been developed.[1] If
maize is untended by human beings for as much as two
years it dies out; it is as dependent on man as the lap dog.
It is the product of untold centuries of breeding, crossing,
and infinite care, bordering on worship. I have seen little
stone idols in the cornfields of modern Mexican Indians,
placed there to make the crop grow.

> The Indian did not know the white man's science but, over
> the millennia, by patience, and thankfully and prayerfully
> accepting favorable mutations, he changed the plant more
> radically than any other plant has ever been changed by man.

Mr. Wallace wrote these eloquent lines before the Brookhaven laboratory went into action, producing mutations
overnight with cobalt 6o. Wherever maize may have originated, by the time of Columbus it had spread over most of
North and South America, including the West Indies. One
of the most intensive areas of corn culture was the dry south-
western corner of what is now the United States. Here the
Hopi Indians of Arizona, among others, practiced dry farming, assisted by magic, prayer sticks, special dances, and the
ritual smoking of tobacco. Their daily life was built around
maize—and still is.

---

[1] Following Henry A. Wallace and W. L. Brown: *Corn* (Michigan State
University Press, 1956).

DATING MAIZE

In a cave in New Mexico, diggers found hundreds of well-preserved corncobs, less than an inch long, together with kernels and tassel fragments. Carbon-14 dating shows them to be about fifty-six hundred years old—older than the rice of China, younger than the wheat of Mesopotamia. They were of the variety called "pod corn," with fifty kernels to the ear. Careful analysis of more recent layers in the cave indicates that over a period of sixteen hundred years, Indian plant breeders increased the length of these cobs from less than an inch to four inches. It was still pod corn at the end of this period, which brings us down to four thousand years ago.

Further investigation disclosed a sudden, spectacular change, this one in Old Mexico. Pod corn was crossed with teosinte, a wild plant known to grow only on the high Mexican plateau. Out of the crossing came a maize close to modern types. "We have a demonstration," says Mr. Wallace, "of how two rather unpromising parents may produce promising offspring." Experiments, combined with religious ceremonies, continued to be made by the Indians. All the major types known today—Flint corn, Flour, Pop, Dent and Sweet—were ultimately produced.

> Fifteen hundred years before the white man came to the New World, these corns had been molded to so high a state that even at that early date, they probably ranked highest among cereals in efficiency of food production. These facts suggest strongly that corn has been cultivated by man much longer than most anthropologists have been willing to conjecture.

Borings into the swampy soil on which Mexico City rests have disclosed further evidence in the shape of fossilized pollen of great antiquity from a plant akin to corn.

Maize, as a storable grain producing an abundant surplus, was developed on the high plateaus of Mexico and in the

uplands of Peru, possibly independently, as we have noted.
The journey on foot over the Isthmus of Panama is, and
was, an exceedingly tough one; but it might have been made
in part by sea. As both cultures also grew the cotton plant
and the yam, it seems possible that there may have been
diffusion at some date. No maize so far as we know was ever
grown in the Old World or on the islands of the Pacific,
until imported from the Americas.

The technique of cultivation resembled that of the first
farmers who invaded Europe, and of Mexican Indians today.
The bush was cut down with stone axes (Indians now use
machetes made in Connecticut), the slash was burned, and
the kernels planted in the ashes with a pointed stick. When
soil fertility gave out, the process was repeated in virgin
bush. It is probable that the shining limestone cities of the
Maya on the high plateau were abandoned because the
cornlands about them became exhausted.

Let us repeat the formula of agriculture, the most important economic formula known to man. The man-hour cost of
subsistence began to decline with the domestication of animals, and fell abruptly with the cultivation of wheat, rice
and maize. This left man-hours free for other activities. The
farmer may have worked as hard as the hunter, but other
members of his group were released. They could now devote
themselves to what we now call "capital improvements"—
to irrigation works, terracing, granaries, towns, and so to
civilization.

A similar pattern developed in all the six centers, five
north of the equator, only Peru to the south. The formula
promoted a sharp increase in population, so long as arable
land held out. Beyond that limit, then as now, the situation
so alarmingly described by Mr. Malthus inevitably arose—
a situation where population outruns its food supply.

9. City Man

THE TIGRIS and the Euphrates rise in the mountains of Turkey, flow roughly parallel southward, then join and empty into the Persian Gulf. Mesopotamia means "between the rivers," and here, according to Herodotus, early farmers could reap two-hundred fold. Fruits were abundant in the area—now known as Iraq—and clay for sun-dried bricks was everywhere. In such a country, to quote H. G. Wells, "men took root as men had never taken root before."

As on a cinema screen, we generalists have watched Homo sapiens, this curious product of evolution, with the big brain, the skillful hand, and the gift of tongues, following the frontiers of the ice, migrating across Siberia, entering North America, hunting in nomad bands over the habitable globe and back again. In his wanderings he accumulated and passed on the key inventions of the bow, the dog, flint tools, techniques for trapping his food supply and for surviving the bitter cold of winter. We have watched him experiment with breeding animals until he shifted from hunter to herdsman, and then experiment with wild grasses until he became, in favored areas, a settled tiller of the soil.

With a two-hundredfold yield, the tiller could take time out for craftwork and other special occupations. Presently, above the surrounding fields of grain, rose the first temples and cities of mankind.

From that day to this the city man has steadily gained in power and numbers over herdsman and farmer, though he could not live without the food they bring him. The people of the United States are now more abundantly fed than any large society in history; yet the farmers, fishermen and ranchers responsible for this bounty constitute only about one worker in eight.

MESOPOTAMIA

This ratio did not hold for the first farmers of Mesopotamia, or its first cities. Indeed we must shift drastically our basis of calculation when we consider them. In the early Sumerian cities, we are told, every citizen was a farmer, raising food for his family in a plot outside the city walls. In addition to this part-time agricultural labor, he might be mason, carpenter, merchant, warehouseman or priest. He was, in fact, a kind of economic generalist. Everyone in town not only knew about farming but practiced it, while nearly everyone also practiced a specialty—a great change from a purely agricultural society.

In London, Tokyo, Chicago, today, such economic generalists have disappeared; every breadwinner is now versed in some specialty, if only ragpicking. In the pioneer days of North America, and in Australia, however, nearly everyone knew about farming, about the care of animals, and how to use field and barn tools—a situation not too different from that of Sumeria.

Before the cities came, the plain between the rivers was dotted with small, self-contained villages, a prosperous, homogeneous population, well rooted and fully exploiting its rich environment.[1] As the villagers acquired skill in draining and irrigating the fields, settlements grew larger. Trad-

---

[1] Following Henri Frankfort: *The Birth of Civilization in the Near East* (Doubleday, 1956).

ers exchanged shells, beads, obsidian and flint. Presently copper was introduced for axes and adzes, bricks were formed and dried in the sun; small temples were erected.

By fifty-five hundred years ago, the settlements had grown into cities built of sun-dried bricks, with towered temples. Ur of the Chaldees was a very early city; later came Mari and still later Babylon. Nineveh was one of the first to build with stone rather than brick. These cities were part of, or developed from, the Sumerian culture, and I shall refer to them frequently as the cities of Sumeria, meaning the earliest known cities on earth.[2] Diggers at Ur have found two-story villas with as many as fourteen rooms, fountains, ovens, and butcher tables for sacrificed animals. In Mari, frescoes which are still bright have been unearthed, also evidence of a long-distance communication system, based on fire signals.

A host of unprecedented problems arrived with the cities —housing, water supply, sanitation, policing, work allotments, records, rationing, temple ceremonials, the need for written messages, and who outranks whom in an emerging class structure. Many of these problems are still with us in Megalopolis. A stimulating variety of new inventions, activities, entertainments and interests arrived too.

How did the first city men solve their unprecedented problems? They had no teachers, remember, no authorities of the past to rely upon. Different cities worked out a variety of political and administrative patterns. Comparing one with another holds a unique fascination, for here, like the print of a hand in plaster, are the known varieties of social systems as they were shaped by elementary and urgent need. Ever since, the patterns have been enlarged and elaborated, with intricate convolutions and incrustations. Look-

---

2 Werner Keller: *The Bible as History* (Morrow, 1956). Jericho, to the west in what is now Jordan, was another very early city. Its oldest houses had round walls like Bedouins' tents, at a time when pottery was still unknown.

ing at the simpler designs of Sumeria, we may better understand the complex patterns of today.

Long ago I was taught by social scientists that the three inventions essential for city living, or civilization, were (1) a storable grain, (2) a beast of burden, and (3) a practical textile. Now I want to argue a little with this definition. Mesopotamia had all three, and so did Egypt, China and India. The civilized people of Peru and Mexico had maize and cotton. Peru domesticated the llama for light loads, but *Mexico had no beast of burden at all.* Thus the rule has its exceptions.

It seems to me, furthermore, that a fourth invention is necessary to civilization, namely, a *written language.* Gibbon, in *The Decline and Fall,* goes so far as to call the use of letters the principal characteristic which distinguishes a civilized people from "a herd of savages." I am not willing to call our neolithic ancestors a herd of savages; but certainly they had no formal writing systems and no cities. Today the surviving nature peoples around the world are unlettered.

PRIESTS AND ACCOUNTANTS

Sumerians shaved their heads and wore a shawl-like woven garment over the left shoulder. All citizens belonged to one of the temples in the city, and were known as "the people of god X." [3] Everyone worked on the canals and dikes, as well as in the fields, and the high priest of the temple assigned the work in a *corvée,* or draft.

All citizens in principle were equal, and all received rations for their work. Money had not been invented; no leisure class existed, and no native serfs. Prisoners of war were sometimes enslaved, but they too were assigned to one of the temples, with *corvée* and rations like citizens.

Does this mean that slavery is a product of civilization? Did the first farmers, and the hunters before them, live in bands where all members were equal? It would seem so in ancient Mesopotamia. Slavery, however, has been practiced

---

[3] Following Frankfort.

for centuries by certain surviving African tribes, who are still in the neolithic stage. We will drop this interesting query in the lap of accredited specialists.

Nomads from the north must have been as astonished at the sight of Ur and Babylon as a Greenland Eskimo today at the sight of Manhattan Island. Each city temple had a high central tower, perhaps for better communication with the gods, perhaps to supervise the population. The temple also had more mundane apartments, such as granaries and storerooms. Here were to be found tools of all kinds, lumber, hides, reeds and rushes, mats; asphalt, valuable building stones like marble; dates, onions and other foods, beer made from barley, wine from grapes.

The high priest was both chief theologian and city manager, allotting the work schedules, tools, raw materials and food rations to all the people of god X. The distribution of goods within the temple community was by allotment, and commodities were also exchanged with other temples in the city. Trade with outside cities was on a barter basis, limited to a few luxuries.

Obviously the high priest had a difficult administrative problem. A system of temple accounts in physical quantities was absolutely necessary if he was to keep the economy under control. The adage that necessity is the mother of invention was fully exemplified in Ur. *Probably the first things ever systematically written down on this planet were bookkeeping records of temple goods in Sumeria.* (As accounting happens to be one of my specialties, I take considerable satisfaction in this historical finding.) These accounts, on clay tablets, might read "beer and bread for one day," thus embracing both quantity and time. Engraved seals identified the parties to a transaction. Gradually the accounting script developed into the complete writing known as cuneiform.

Clay tablets dug up at Ur record warehouse supplies, spinning mills owned by the temple, workers' names and rations, wool given to workers and garments woven therefrom, legal decisions and sentences of criminals. At Mari, twenty-four thousand tablets have been found, many still undeciphered. They include a list of two thousand craftsmen, and orders for the construction of canals, locks and dams on the Euphrates.

EGYPT

How did civilization develop in Egypt, that ribbon of agriculture along the Nile? The Egyptians apparently invented writing later than the Sumerians. Their early hieroglyphics, however, recorded not transactions in beer and bread, but achievements of the royal family. Their political organization was entirely different. Instead of a number of autonomous cities surrounded by fields, the Nile provided a single tilled strip, with villages and towns spaced at intervals, and only a few cities for religious ceremonials, such as Memphis. Egypt from the First Dynasty on (approximately five thousand years ago) was a monolithic theocracy, ruled by a god-king, called Pharaoh and so exalted that he could marry only his sister.

The citizen of Egypt was less free than the citizen of Mesopotamia, but he had certain rights, and could appeal to a high court for justice. There was no ironclad caste system and no race prejudice; a peasant boy could rise on merit to the highest administrative post, and so could a dark-skinned Nubian.

Egyptians, like Mesopotamians, were liable to *corvée* for public works and pyramid building, carried on in those seasons of the year when the Nile did not require their undivided attention. There was some private internal trading by means of barter, but Pharaoh did all the export and import business, again confined mostly to luxuries.

The Nile enforced a single political state. Pharaoh was the vicar of the gods and an absolute monarch, but his rule was not regarded by the people as tyranny, nor his service as slavery.[4] Egyptians appear to have been conservative and obedient but not abject; there were no major uprisings against Pharaoh over a period of three thousand years. The Nile with its spring deposit of fertile soil gave more economic security than the Tigris and Euphrates, but the political structure was authoritarian, quite unlike the early democracy of Mesopotamia.

Egypt developed a sophisticated culture long before the building of the pyramids. In the flat tombs of the early Pharaohs, recent diggings show that everything was provided for the occupant to make life comfortable in the hereafter. The ruler lay on his right side within a large wooden sarcophagus. Beyond were vaults containing furniture inlaid with ivory, toilet implements, and games. Alabaster dishes held ribs of beef, pigeons, quail, fish, fruits, bread and cake. Other vaults contained tall jars of wine, elaborate clothing, tools and agricultural equipment, weapons of flint and copper, all the accessories of a well-organized civilization. These tombs were built and stocked some five thousand years ago, and in them, thanks to the cult of immortality, we can follow the customs of living in early Egypt in minute detail.

TWO CULTURES COMPARED

There was some diffusion at this stage between Egypt and Mesopotamia. Scholars are not yet agreed on who originated what, but as I read the record the two cultures seem to have started independently. Both had the agricultural background and the drive to produce an indigenous civilization. We know indigenous cultures grew up in the New World; why not on the Euphrates and on the Nile as well? They differed widely, as we have seen; Egypt was far more autocratic than Mesopotamia and more stable politically. In the latter, the cities soon began to quarrel; empire builders like Sargon I tried to unify the region, but

---

4 Following Frankfort.

unification did not stick. There was also much trouble with invading tribes, which Egypt was largely spared.

Yet, amid the melee, we have a fine example of the under-lying strength and continuity of a society, contrasted with the kings, conquerors and high priests on the top. Political history deals with the top layer, but the true story lies deeper. H. G. Wells makes this point brilliantly in his review of Mesopotamia:

> Meanwhile the plow does its work year by year, the harvests are gathered, the builders build . . . , the tradesmen work and acquire fresh devices; the knowledge of writing spreads; novel things, the horse and wheeled vehicles and iron are intro-duced and become part of the permanent inheritance of man-kind; the volume of trade upon sea and desert increases, men's ideas widen and knowledge grows. There are set-backs, massacres, pestilence. . . . For 4000 years this new thing, civilization, which had set its root into the soil of the two rivers, grew as a tree grows, now losing a limb, now stripped by a storm, but always growing. . . . It changed its dominant race; it changed its language, but it remained essentially the same development. After 4000 years the warriors and con-querors were still going to and fro over this growing thing they did not understand. . . .[5]

Do the warriors and conquerors, the prime ministers and presidents, understand it any better today?

CHINA AND INDIA

Chinese legendary history tells about gods, emperors and palaces, dating back five thousand years. It tells of a great flood about four thousand years ago, which must have been a local tidal wave or a river flood. Archaeologists have de-scribed the thriving villages and terraced fields. After the rice fields were established, towns and cities began to rise, as in Mesopotamia.

The first kingdom was that of the Shang dynasty, begin-

---

[5] *Outline of History.* Wells includes the farming era to get his 4,000 years, 7,000 to 3,000 years ago.

ning thirty-five hundred years ago. Bronze tools and weapons had been developed by that time, indicating that tin and copper were mined and smelted (10 per cent of tin hardens 90 per cent of copper into bronze). Horses and chariots, cowrie shells as money, religious observances and divination were in evidence, and sculptured stonework adorned the cities. There were apparently two centers of civilization in China, south and north, probably in close contact exchanging their knowledge and invention. An intricate and comprehensive system of writing was developed early, one which has not greatly changed to this day.

Diggers in 1922 at Harappa, now Pakistan, laid bare an unsuspected civilization that flourished in India long before the Aryan people invaded from the north. It appears to be at least forty-five hundred years old, a thousand years older than Chinese civilization, a thousand years younger than Mesopotamian. Populous cities based on the usual surplus of grain, probably wheat, were built of red brick. Each city had an imposing citadel, the center of government and religion, where a mother-goddess was worshiped. There were central granaries and well-engineered water and drainage systems. Arts and crafts were highly sophisticated, and a fully developed system of writing is indicated by inscriptions on stone seals, not yet deciphered. Scholars think that writing was chiefly done on materials like leather and textiles which have since disintegrated.

HIGH CULTURE IN AFRICA

A curious footnote comes from the Belgian Congo, where archaeologists have unearthed the remains of the Ishango people, living some eight thousand years ago, long before the first cities in Mesopotamia. The Ishango built no cities, but they used "a primitive abacus or multiplication table, probably the oldest in the world." [6] It consisted of a cylindrical piece of bone about four inches long, inscribed with

---

[6] *New York Times*, June 9, 1957.

an orderly series of scratches, adding up to 60. Scientists
who found it think the cylinder might also have been used
as a stylus for writing, or perhaps as a tattooing tool. Tattooing and even a primitive number system in a hunting
culture we can well believe, but surely not a stylus for real
writing! Herdsmen need to count their flocks; even hunters
may wish to count their arrows, but writing comes only with
cities.

Sites of cities may eventually be found and excavated in
Africa. What little work has been done south of Egypt has
disclosed remains which are both significant and very ancient. The continent will bear watching by generalists, as
well as archaeologists.

WRITING AND COUNTING

Though language will be the subject of a later chapter,
the invention of writing definitely belongs here. The first
formal writing so far known was the inventory of stocks in
Mesopotamian temples, and ever since the connection between writing and counting in civilized cultures has been
close. It is impossible to carry on the business of an urban
community without a number system, a calendar and a
means to record and communicate orders, edicts and laws.
Oral communication tends to be distorted with every rep-
etition.

Specialists divide writing into three stages: pictographic,
ideographic, phonetic. Let us look briefly at each.

1. *Pictographic.* In this first stage, a deer hunt will be
represented by a drawing of a man throwing a spear. Such
literal form of writing is fairly common in hunting cultures
—North American Indians used it—but is useless for city
administrators, to say nothing of poets and writers. I should
find some difficulty inscribing this paragraph in pictographs.

2. *Ideographic.* Little symbols, many of them pictures,
stand for collections or categories of things—such as men,
cows, gods, war, water, plowing, days—rather than a specific deer hunt. In Chinese script, "war" is represented by

three women under a gate. The ideograph for "trouble" is two women. Whatever else the ancient Chinese invented, they do not seem to have invented feminism.

3. *Phonetic.* In these more advanced writing systems, signs and symbols no longer stand for ideas at all but only for *sounds*, which in combination denote ideas. The sign may represent a whole syllable, or only a letter of the alphabet. The former has been found clumsy in use, and most modern cultures have come around to the alphabet. Red China is now attempting to bring the old ideographic script up to date with a modern alphabet. The Chinese student has had to learn thousands of signs to write his language, where the English student needs to learn only twenty-six letters and the ten digits, o to 9.

Here is the way the word "ox" developed in Mesopotamia: [7]

WORD "OX"

ORIGINAL PICTOGRAPH	
LATER CUNEIFORM	
EARLY BABYLONIAN	
ASSYRIAN	

The Mesopotamians began with a stylized picture of an oxhead with horns, and gradually worked around in the Assyrian language to something having no clear connection with an ox. Sometimes, however, they began with a purely abstract sign that bore no resemblance to the referent. A sheep, for instance, was ⊕. By the time cuneiform characters came into use, writing had advanced from the ideographic far into the phonetic stage.

Egyptian hieroglyphic writing also advanced into the

[7] After Frankfort.

phonetic stage as some of the signs became alphabetical. Mexican writing, as we shall see, remained ideographic, while the Peruvians employed something called a quipu, still an enigma, but certainly used for counting. The Maya Indians of Mexico invented one of the world's great numerical systems, based on 20 rather than 10, complete with a zero notation.

We now turn to the first civilizations and cities of the Western Hemisphere. Some knowledge of them is important for all generalists, but to those of us who happen to live in the West, an account of their achievements holds a unique interest.

10 . Cities of the West

NO CONNECTION has ever been established between the early civilizations of the Eastern and Western Hemispheres. Scholars are reasonably sure that Stone Age hunters came over Bering Strait, followed thousands of years later by an Eskimo people who spread along the arctic shore to Greenland. The hunters seem to have made their way down to Panama, and traversed or sailed past the isthmus. By nine thousand years ago they had reached the Strait of Magellan. Evidence of early fishermen and food gatherers, as well as hunters, is found throughout South America. There were settlements of an advanced neolithic culture at the mouth of the Amazon.

The Stone Age people from Asia brought harpoons, axes and other implements and techniques which shaped their life in the Americas. No artifacts from the *cities* of China, Mesopotamia or Egypt have ever been found. Perhaps even more important, linguists have been unable to trace any relationship between the known languages of East and West.

Similar human needs and problems, however, animated the people of both regions. A similar formula was followed in favored areas, and two civilizations arose on maize in the West, as four had arisen on wheat and rice in the East. We call the former "Peru" and "Mexico," largely, I suspect, because of Prescott's immortal histories. Actually the Peruvian empire at its peak included parts of modern Colombia,

99

Ecuador, Bolivia, Chile and Argentina, as well as Peru. The "Mexican" civilization included cities in Guatemala and Honduras as well as the Yucatán peninsula and the Mexican plateau.

PERU

Intensive agriculture first appeared on the slopes of the Peruvian Andes and in settlements along the Pacific coast. The coast people had flint tools, baskets, mats, and cloth made by twisting cotton fibers. They flourished about four thousand years ago, according to carbon-14 dating. During the next thousand years, both coast and highland people developed maize, the weaving of true textiles, adobe bricks, irrigation works and complicated religious systems. This period parallels in a rough way the agricultural development of Mesopotamia before the first cities.

Some time around three thousand years ago, the Peruvians began to build cities and temples. The builders used enormous blocks of cut stone, weighing up to forty tons, and fitted too closely to admit the proverbial knife blade. At Cuzco, and south of Lake Titicaca, archaeologists find imposing ruins erected long before the Incas. They indicate a civilization in command of large labor armies, and remind us of the *corvées* which built the pyramids of Egypt. Archaeologists call this era the "classic period," a time of low-relief carving on stone and magnificent craftsmanship in textiles, pottery and polished flints.

THE INCAS

Nobody yet knows where the Incas of Peru came from. They seem to have been a relatively small but highly dynamic tribe. One guess is that they came over the Pacific in large canoes, but what is known of their language shows no affiliation with the languages of the Pacific islands. They established themselves in Peru about 1000 A.D., bringing the "classic period" to a close. By the time Pizarro arrived with his muskets and horses in 1532, the Incas had conquered and organized an empire extending down the backbone of the Andes from Ecuador to Chile.

The Incas built new stone cities, and mined gold, silver, copper and tin. From these metals and their alloys, especially bronze, they made axes, knives, digging sticks, breastplates, masks, earplugs, necklaces. The West thus had its Bronze Age as well as the East, but thousands of years later. It never had an Iron Age. The Inca god-king dined on solid gold and silver service—a circumstance which was to bring out the least amiable traits in the Spanish invaders. Pottery was ornamented with as many as eight colors, in designs which depicted plants, animals and hunting scenes. Textiles, including handsome tapestries, were woven of cotton, wool, alpaca and vicuña, and dyed with colors which did not fade.

The Inca empire is usually called a form of state socialism, but I think of it rather as something unique, fitting no political category. At its head was the Inca, both king and sun god, with a huge bureaucracy under him. Like Pharaoh, he was so exalted that he could marry only his sister. As in Mesopotamia and Egypt, the *corvée* was general for public works. All produce belonged to the state, and rations were allotted to citizens. Central granaries were filled with maize, not only for the current food supply, but to provide a reserve against drought and crop failures. Craftsmen were allotted their raw materials from public stores. An enforced colonization of uninhabited areas seems to have been practiced, something pretty close to slavery.

Boys were brought up to continue the occupation of their fathers—farmer, herdsman, craftsman, miner. They could not move to another town or marry outside their station. Narrow roads of stone were constructed up and down the Andes, covering four thousand miles of latitude, sometimes cut into the face of perpendicular cliffs, and leading to towns as high as sixteen thousand feet. What a contrast with Egypt, another long, narrow empire, but occupying the flat plain of the Nile!

THE QUIPU

Before me as I write is a photograph of Mr. Ollantay Suarez of Lima, Peru, the twenty-sixth Inca by direct descent. His last reigning ancestor, Atahualpa, was executed four centuries ago by order of the conquistador Pizarro. Suarez, a pleasant-looking young man of twenty-one, with a crew cut, sits on the steps of the library of Columbia University. He is a sophomore, specializing appropriately in anthropology, and already he has discovered ancient carvings in a cave near Lake Titicaca. He is wearing an embroidered Inca headdress, and holds a quipu between his knees. This curious artifact is constructed around a crossbar perhaps three feet long, from which hangs a series of knotted ropes and strings, in many colors and richly decorated. The longest string might be three feet, making the whole contraption roughly a yard square.

In the Inca empire, runners carried official decrees from station to station on the royal roads by means of the quipu. Originally it seems to have been an invention for keeping track of numbers like an abacus. As time went on certain laws and edicts could be communicated by the order in which the knots on the strings were tied. In every place of importance, we are told, there was an official whose business it was to interpret quipu and to make quipu—that is, read the knots, and tie them. Some students go so far as to suggest that the knots could convey astronomical information.

Whatever the quipu could or could not convey, it was a clumsy communication device compared with those worked out in the other five centers of civilization. Let the reader ascend the royal dais, eat and drink his fill from dishes of beaten gold, and then try to run a country four thousand miles long with a quipu—with a whole lot of quipus. Puzzling over this enigma, I cannot help wondering if the Incas did not invent a practical system of written communication which has so far escaped the archaeologists. Perhaps they used flimsy material, as in India, which has altogether disappeared; perhaps samples are still preserved in some unexplored caves. Quipus might do for backward provincials, but hardly for the officials in the capital. It would require an outsized brain to administer a far-flung empire with the implement I see on the lap of Señor Suarez. He looks bright, but not that bright.

One reason for the sudden collapse of his ancestral empire was a palace revolution. When Pizarro landed, the royal power was in dispute, a situation which seriously confused the Inca bureaucrats and generals. Who was to give orders? Pizarro boldly exploited this power crisis.

MEXICO

The Spanish conquerors reported no contact between the cultures of Peru and Mexico, though both had the cotton plant and the yam. In addition, the Peruvians had the potato as a staple food and had invented bronze, which was unknown in Mexico. The Mexicans in turn were far ahead in written language, mathematics and astronomy.

The Aztecs, with their capital on the present site of Mexico City, at nearly eight thousand feet, were the major power to oppose Cortes, but they were only the last of a series of high cultures in Mexico and Central America. Nobody knows who built the great structures at Teotihuacán, where the Pyramid of the Sun is said to contain as much stone as the pyramid of Cheops in Egypt. Toltec, Mixtec, Zapotec were other renowned high cultures, but greatest of all were the Maya—architects, scientists and artists.

Four or five thousand years ago a hunting people, speaking a Maya language, lived in the high country of what is now Guatemala, and the Mexican state of Chiapas.[1] By three thousand years ago these people had developed maize, fine pottery and textiles, and had evolved a vigesimal

1 Following Sylvanus G. Morley: *The Ancient Maya* (Stanford University Press, 1946). This section will be largely based on his work.

number system, based on toes as well as fingers—a zero and nineteen signs. Here is the way it looked, carved on stone or inscribed on codices of paper.

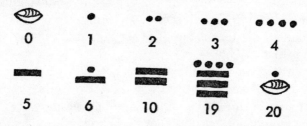

About twenty-three hundred years ago, the Maya priests, for the first time in the history of the human race, devised a system of numeration by position, involving the conception and use of the mathematical quantity of zero, a tremendous achievement in intellectual abstraction. Our own decimal system, with its priceless zero, was invented by the Hindus in India about 800 A.D., more than a thousand years later. From India it entered Europe via Arabia and the Moors, but did not come into general use until 1400 A.D., two thousand years after the Maya had begun their calculations. Theirs was a better numerical system than anything invented in the other centers, better indeed than the Roman system, which lacked a zero.

CALENDAR

Using their nineteen digits and a zero, Maya scientists went on to develop an accurate calendar. Over the centuries they determined by observations that the length of the year was 365.24+ days (modern astronomers figure it at 365.2422), and the length of the lunar month 29.52+ days. With these two calculations in hand they proceeded to construct a calendar more exact than anything known until recent times.

Morley, poring over the records, suggests that this calendar may have been the work of a single mind, "some ancient Maya Hipparchus, who brought the chronological system to perfection in his own lifetime." Whether the calendar had one inventor or several, the Maya historical record begins with a year corresponding to our 353 B.C.[2] From then on, temples and buildings were probably dated on wood, which has since disintegrated. The first firm date on an upright stone stela corresponds to 328 A.D., 681 years after the beginning of the historical record.

There are scores of Maya cities, both in the highlands and on the plains of Yucatán. To visit Chichén Itzá or Uxmal, even in their partially restored state, with the great white terraced pyramids rising above the green jungle, is an experience one never forgets.[3] Stelas are found in all the ancient cities, with dates carved to commemorate some historical or religious event. Combined with bars and dots and zeros are pictograms, or glyphs, in the distinctive Maya style, like nothing else on earth, signifying days, months and years. A tun or 360-day period has, for instance, this glyph:

A stela is thus a combination of art and science, a lovely piece of sculpture in low relief, announcing an elaborately calculated date.

MAYA WRITING

These people also made use of certain characters or letters, with which they wrote in their books their ancient affairs and their sciences, and with these drawings and with certain signs in these drawings, they understood their affairs and made others understand them, and taught them. We found a great number of books in these characters, and, as they contained

---

nothing in them in which was not to be seen superstition and lies of the devil, we burned them all, which they regretted to an amazing degree and caused them affliction.

The burning of the books in Yucatán, thus described by Bishop Landa,[4] caused affliction not only to the local Maya librarians, but to every scholar and student of history since that day. Only three Maya codices survived the holocaust, having earlier been sent back to Spain as mementos. The writing and drawings are inscribed on a folio made from wood pulp, held together by native gum. The Spaniards burned all the other books they could get their hands on, and doubtless felt virtuous in doing so.

The Maya, according to Morley, had graduated from the pictograph stage of writing to the ideograph. Their symbols had come to stand for abstract classes, like "men," "gods," "maize." It is now possible to read about one-third of their hieroglyphics, especially matters concerned with the calendar, astronomy, seasons for planting and harvesting. The three surviving codices deal with religious ceremonies, horoscopes and divinations. Those so ruthlessly destroyed might have thrown a great light on Maya history and science, "a treasure house that would have cleared up many a mystery. . . ."

The Spaniards in effect decapitated the maize culture of Mexico, both Aztec on the plateau and Maya in Yucatán, by superseding the intellectual class and obliterating their records. The Maya intellectuals were a relatively small group of temple priests, with a tight monopoly on learning. "This awesome knowledge of the movements of the heavenly bodies, this ability to predict eclipses, and the path of Venus, must have been a source of tremendous power to the priesthood." It kept the common people in ignorance as well as in awe and humility. No generalists were allowed to develop among them.

---

4 As quoted by Morley.

When the priesthood was wiped out, the common people had no way to maintain their arts and sciences. Part of their superlative craftsmanship remained, and still glows in the native handicrafts of Mexico and Guatemala. The Spaniards distorted the culture of the common people, but were never able to stamp it out, as did the Anglo-Saxons to the north. In one sense the Indians of Mexico absorbed their conquerors, as other people—the Chinese, for instance—are said to have done. But the shining cities, the ball courts, the sculpture, the painting, the astronomy and mathematics ended forever and the jungle closed in.

The Maya in their great period in the highlands, around 600 A.D., seem to have practiced human sacrifice, though sparingly, according to Morley. By the time they had migrated to the lowlands of Yucatán, and had considerable contact with the Aztecs, the practice was widespread, and we can give the Spaniards due credit for eliminating it. The Spanish themselves got over the bloodletting of the Inquisition. Whether the Mexicans would have grown out of the horrid rite of human sacrifice we shall never know. It may well have been an element in their destruction, when the supreme test came from Cortes and Alvarado.

Why did the Maya leave their elaborate cities and sculptured monuments on the highlands, around 800 A.D.? Morley believes that the most probable cause was the exhaustion of the soil. The fields of maize were finally forced out too far for transportation by manpower (there was no beast of burden), and city living became untenable. Even in fertile Yucatán, there is clear evidence that the city of Chichén Itzá was abandoned for two hundred years, presumably to let nature restore enough humus to revive the cornfields.

The maize cultures of Mexico had great promise, but two fatal defects developed. Their agricultural techniques were too wasteful to support permanent cities, and their learning was concentrated in too few hands. We can be absolutely sure, with our modern knowledge of biology, that the Maya elite did not possess all the brains in the society. Owing to a tight monopoly of learning, the whole culture became vulnerable, both in Mexico and in Peru under the Incas. Could there be a more impressive argument for a wide diffusion of knowledge?

The words of Bernal Díaz, soldier of Cortes, remain to haunt us, as he came up from Veracruz to the Valley of Mexico:

> Gazing on such wonderful sights, we did not know what to say, or whether what appeared before us was real. On one side, on the land, there were great cities, and in the lake [Texcoco] many more, and in the causeway were many bridges at intervals, and in front of us stood the great city of Mexico, and . . . the palaces how spacious and well built they were, of beautiful stone work and cedar wood. . . . Great canoes were able to pass into the gardens from the lake outside. And all was ornamented and very splendid with many kinds of stone monuments with pictures on them. Then the birds of many kinds which came into the garden. I say again that I stood looking at it and thought that never in the world would there be discovered such lands as these. Of all the wonders that I then beheld, today all is overthrown and lost, nothing is standing.

CIVILIZATION IS ORGANIZATION

The six centers of early civilization which we have outlined in the last two chapters can be dated in round figures:

	Years Ago
Mesopotamia	5,500
Egypt	5,000
India	4,500
China	3,500
Peru	3,000
Mexico	3,000

Other Old World centers, such as Crete and Mycenae, while earlier than Peru and Mexico, were offshoots of Mesopotamia and Egypt, or heavily influenced by them. The first seafaring culture was developed on the island of Crete.

Homo sapiens as a hunter needed language, fire, flint, tools and weapons, skin clothing, pots, fibers. He needed a family system to rear his children, and a dog to help in the hunt. He needed leaders, and a certain amount of organization within the band, especially when a mammoth was to be trapped. In winter he could use a good cave, if one was available. He needed medical care for sickness and accidents, but the science of medicine was unknown. What happened when he broke his leg? Did he die, like a deer or a horse?

As husbandman, his economic needs expanded to include stockbreeding, slash-and-burn field making, irrigation, the wheel, equipment for plowing, sowing, harvesting and storing grain. He took time off to express his artistic sense in decorating pottery and textiles. He began to think about the gods, the hereafter and the proper disposal of the dead.

The first city men incorporated as many of these inventions and developments as seemed to them useful, and began a spiral of cultural advance which today, fifty-five hundred years later, is still swirling upward.

Biological change, however, has not been in evidence. Anthropologists affirm that if a Stone Age baby were brought up in New York, he would root for the Yankee baseball team, like everybody else, and perhaps graduate from Columbia. *Per contra*, New York babies, brought up on the edge of the ice, would make as good hunters as anybody else—no better. Neither mind nor body has undergone appreciable evolution during the last fifty thousand years.[5] The Atomic Age, as contrasted with the Stone Age, is a purely cultural phenomenon, the culmination of invention piled on invention, custom upon custom, belief system upon belief system, all

---

5 Medical science works both ways: it keeps a lot of chronically sick people alive who would have died off in the Stone Age, such as diabetics; it cures a lot of people who would be dragging around half-alive. The net effect on the "pool of genes" is anybody's guess.

handed down with the help of language, from generation to generation.

Early city men constructed other solid artifacts along with their cities—ships, canals, dams, aqueducts, war chariots, underground tombs, stelas. They opened trade routes for caravans, and market centers which called for accounting methods and presently money. Agricultural seasons and the storing of grain necessitated calendars, as did the proper days for placating and celebrating the gods.

In Mesopotamia, temple bookkeeping inaugurated the first formal writing system. All six centers developed non-vocal communication, although it is hard to conceive the Inca quipu as a medium for administering a great empire.

The complex religious systems which arose with the first cities were not an unmixed blessing. Dogma, absolutism, theocracy, rigid ideologies do not always make for peace, while human sacrifice, as part of the religious ceremonials of Mexico, is utterly abhorrent to us.

Among the most significant changes brought by civilization were the shift in the size of the group, and the position of the individual within the group. Homo sapiens gave up the relatively free life and the rough democracy of the roving band in open country, to become an organization man, for organization is as necessary to city living as brick and stone. A compact colony of occupational specialists is impossible without rules, laws, public services, policemen. We have no inherited equipment to take care of such matters; all must be worked out by the culture. There must be administrators to direct them, and every citizen must learn his place in relation to them.

In these circumstances, political systems become inevitable. We have glanced at the democracy of early Sumeria, the autocracy of Egypt and Peru, the theocracy of Mexico. When the interests of two organized city states clashed, organized warfare tended to follow, with its elaborate paraphernalia of weapons, drilling, strategy and tactics. Was it at this point, only about five thousand years ago, that men began killing men against whom they had no personal grievance, simply because they were regimented to do so? One wonders.

City living encouraged class systems, legal systems, a governing elite, bureaucracy, serfdom and slavery. The *corvée* for public works required meticulous organization. It is clear that the invention of a storable grain created as many problems as it solved. More security, yes, and more difficulties.

Ever since civilization began, various seers and poets and reformers have called upon their fellows to renounce the luxuries and sinfulness of cities and return to the simple life. Some seers, such as Rousseau, have pointed to the noble savage, others to the uncomplicated virtues of the man with the hoe. Today in America, with only about 12 per cent of the working force left on the land, popular morality is still solidly based on the self-sufficient farmer celebrated by Thomas Jefferson—a fine illustration of cultural lag.

Such complaints are voices in the wind. Civilization is on a massive trend curve, and for better or worse, increasing numbers of us must live in it, or with it. India, China, Africa, South America, all are determined to industrialize today. There is no retreat, but this does not mean that we cannot contrive a pleasanter place to live than Megalopolis.

11 . History for Generalists

SO FAR in this book, we have been outlining a kind of generalist's history of man and his environment, from the formation of the solar system to the first cities. The bulk of the record lies in the area of prehistory, or unwritten history, for no written word about it was ever preserved until the clay tablets of Ur carried their accounting for bread and beer.

We have observed, however, that the record derived from the digs, deductions, and measurements of archaeologists, geologists and other specialists may be more accurate in some respects than the story carried by the written documents on which accredited historians must rely.

Our path has been reasonably direct, for although we were running lines all over the planet, we had a fairly straight road of progress to follow. Through the eons of the earth's formation and cooling, and the later eons of emerging life, changes were slow. Glacially slow would be an understatement, for glaciers are rapid compared with the upthrusting of mountains, or with living things which modify through countless generations.

In the first few millennia after the development of true man, the changes still were slow. We have noted that they were different in *kind*, for this strange product of biological evolution ceased to evolve. Instead of adapting his body to environmental conditions, he devised equipment with which to meet the conditions, and gradually he began to mold the environment itself.

DATES IN UNWRITTEN HISTORY

A timetable may prove helpful at this point. The dates of course are rough, but they serve to give a sequence and perspective, as generalists from many cultures peer into their common past.

	Years ago
Formation of the earth, perhaps	4.5 billion
Beginning of life in the sea, about	2 billion
First land animals, about	300 million
First mammals, about	70 million
Proto-man evolved, perhaps	1 million
First true man, with big brain and language, perhaps	250,000
Modern-type man, at least	50,000
Retreat of last ice age began, perhaps	40,000
Stone Age man crossed into North America, perhaps	25,000
First farmers in Mesopotamia, about	7,000
First cities in Mesopotamia, about	5,500
First cities in Egypt, about	5,000
First cities in India (pre-Aryan), perhaps	4,500
First cities in China, about	3,500
First cities in Peru (pre-Inca), about	3,000
First cities in Mexico, about	3,000

With the establishment of cities, civilization, aided by writing and systems for counting, fanned out in many directions. Simpler people learned from the more advanced, and imitated them. Diffusion from Mesopotamia and Egypt, or perhaps actual groups of colonizers, helped to found the fabulous city of Knossos in Crete, capital of the first seafaring state. Mesopotamia and Egypt, one or both, were responsible for ancient Mycenae in Greece, for cities along the North African coast, and presently for urban communities in Southern and Western Europe and Britain.

Chinese centers spread to Manchuria, Korea, Japan. A neolithic people were in Japan perhaps five thousand years ago, with flourishing farms and villages by the time of the Christian era. Japanese civilization with cities and dynasties began about 400 A.D. Chinese culture also spread south to Indochina, Malaya and Burma. In due course the fabulous sculptured towers of Angkor were built—still to astonish modern eyes.

The civilization of India was spreading during the same period. It influenced peoples to the north; southward it established cultural colonies in Ceylon, Java and out into the South Pacific. Many localities were influenced by both India and China—as reflected in the name "Indochina"—but Australia was never reached; its people remained in the Stone Age until the Europeans came.

Off the north coast of Australia lies Melville Island, so isolated that its natives, the Tiwi, "thought for centuries that they were the only people in existence"—thereby outdoing Ptolemy in racial complacency. Much more digging and dating is needed before all the radial lines from early China and India can be firmly mapped.

The early maize cultures of Peru and Mexico sent branches up and down the Andes, out to islands in the Caribbean Sea, up to the mound builders of the Ohio Valley in North America. Indian corn saved the lives of the Pilgrim Fathers at Plymouth, Massachusetts, during their first hard winter. The Inca and Maya centers themselves, however, were decapitated, as we have seen.

THE MAZE OF HISTORY

The student who wishes to know what happened next is confronted with a problem. To continue the linear progression is impossible. Six branches might be followed one by one, but when all six begin to proliferate at a geometric rate, the student finds himself in a maze, an endlessly alluring one. Shadowy passages, leading in all directions, tempt him to bring flashlight and tools to explore some byway which others may have overlooked.

The known historical avenues also beckon the reader, with the lure of travel enhanced by the added dimension of time. With a shelf of books and a lively imagination, one can spend days, if not years, picturing the glory that was Greece and the grandeur that was Rome, in an escape from the worries and problems of the present. Even more than finding out what happens next, one may want to experience the "imaginative reconstruction of the past," in Morris Cohen's phrase, drawing on both science and art. He may crave to know how it *felt* to follow Moses to the Promised Land, or Xerxes or Genghis Khan, or step with Columbus upon the soil of Hispaniola. He would like to hear Haydn conduct the Farewell Symphony for the first time at Esterhazy, and see Shakespeare on the stage of the Globe Theater.

Whether the student skips at haphazard from century to century and continent to continent, or burrows into an historical specialty, he has left the path of a generalist. There is of course a main track, marked out in school and college. After following this for a few years, the student will be equipped to pass a regents' examination, or answer Mr. Gallup's questions in the "cultural Olympics."

This main-track history is largely written in terms of dynasties, wars and conquests, the fortunes of what Communists in Moscow quaintly call "ruling circles." Exciting accounts trace the shifts of power, the dynamism of war and conquest, the building of great cities, the rise of empires and their disappearance. The reader tends to forget the energy of nature in marveling at the furious energy of man as he builds and invents, multiplies, migrates and fights. Yet it is of course the energy of nature, expressing itself in myriad human forms, in a human upheaval that for five millennia has flowered and multiplied and accelerated, with no clearly foreseeable diminution.

For every written account in the historic period, moreover, many more remain unwritten. Troy and her epic are immortal, but Troy was a small city. Had there been a hundred Homers, a hundred other cities might have yielded stories equally absorbing. Alexander's amazing conquests were well documented, but not those of the Incas, which might have proved even more astonishing. As one follows Napoleon or Hitler about the map, he cannot help being impressed by the impermanence of boundaries and nations, the undependability of anything political and military but change.

Clearly the generalist cannot hope to charge his memory with all the marchings and countermarchings of ruling circles from the rise of Babylon to the fall of Berlin. Even if he could absorb this knowledge, and possessed total recall into the bargain, what should he conclude from it? So brilliant a scholar as Arnold Toynbee has had little success in establishing laws of civilization which other competent scholars will accept.

I have recently reread H. G. Wells's *Outline of History*, to find that it produces no over-all conclusion in my mind about "history" as such; no convictions that "history proves" anything, or that "the judgment of history" is in any way final. But the book is useful in providing references and background for what happened in Jerusalem, Lydia or Athens, and how writing began, and where Alexander the Great went.

As generalists we are in some semantic difficulty at this point. What should we know about "history"? Indeed, what is "history"? The word alone, despite its wide use, means little more than "prior events." One must take a further step to get real meaning, and ask "events about what?" If the "what" includes all that has happened to all peoples since Sumeria, the mind reels. But if it means information about Ancient Athens, or the American Civil War, or Moslem sects, then "history" comes alive.

A historian can hardly specialize in history—just history —any more than a scientist can specialize in science. There is an historical *method*, as there is a scientific method. This historical method aids a specialist in selecting sources, comparing and judging evidence, when he is trying to determine what actually happened at a given place and a given time in the past. Historians, whether teachers or writers, specialize on the *history of something*, of some events a good deal more limited than the whole canvas of the past. Gibbon specialized on the decline of Rome, Prescott on the conquest of Peru, Churchill on World War II, among other things.

Specialists in other subjects, however, often find themselves studying history too. Indeed, one might argue that "history" is not so much an independent science as it is the handmaiden of more specific disciplines. Thus one studies modern economics and, for background, the history of economic thought. One studies the history of mechanical invention, of architecture, of clipper ships, canal building, the city of Paris, of psychoanalysis, or choral music. A famous book by a doctor, *Rats, Lice and History*, relates medical history to political change.

Thus history, like so many other subjects, turns out to be not absolute but relative. It is relative also in another important sense—that is, its significance changes for different people at different times, and it has to be rewritten. We raise an eyebrow at the mad scrambles of Russian encyclopedists who have to rewrite the record with every major change in the party line. But something not too dissimilar happens on this side of what we call the Iron Curtain. Listen to the words of a great generalist, Herbert J. Muller (not to be confused with Hermann J. Muller, who specializes in genetics) in his book *The Uses of the Past*:

> Simply to state "what has actually happened" . . . is far from being a simple business, even apart from the fact that we can never hope to know all that has actually happened. . . . The main problem is . . . to make sense out of the vast deal that we do know. . . .
>
> The most objective history conceivable is still a selection and an interpretation. . . . The past has no meaningful existence except as it exists for us, as it is given meaning by us. In piety and justice we try to see it as it was, or as it seemed

to the men who lived it, but even this poetic interest is not disinterested; in our contemplation of the drama we see what is most pertinent for our own hopes and fears. Hence the past keeps changing with the present. Every age has to rewrite its history, re-create the past . . . the Peloponnesian War and the decline of the Roman Empire have a special significance for us that they could not have had for the Middle Ages or the Renaissance; by the same token, they will have a different significance for a Hindu or Chinese than for a Western historian. Our task is to create a "usable past," for our own living purposes.

Yet this admission of relativity does not permit us to create whatever we have a mind to, make over the past to suit ourselves. Old Testament and early Christian historians could freely tamper with the facts because they knew the divine plan of history. . . . Our distinctive interests and beliefs make it possible for history to be relatively disinterested and impartial. Through Marx, Freud, Sumner, Pareto, Boas, Spengler, and many others, we have become more aware of the inveterate habit of rationalization and the sources of bias— the class interests, the *mores,* the conditioned reflexes of culture, the unconscious assumptions, the "climate of opinion." . . .

THREE COURSES OF ACTION

The generalist, avoiding specialization by definition, still wonders what he shall do in the premises. What is useful knowledge about "history" for the fifty centuries since Ur? I suggest that he might do three things:

First, he can deliberately turn specialist in respect to his own country, not an intensive specialist of course, but enough to capture the outline of its development and its relations to other countries. He can extend this study to his own broad civilization, whether Arabic, European, East Indian, Chinese.

Second, he can choose for study some other country and period, both to experience the delights of exploration and to acquire perspective by comparison with his own culture. For Americans, I would suggest a country in the Orient:

Japan, Iran, Thailand; for Orientals, the reverse: France, Sweden, the United States.

Third, he can acquire an understanding of the great cultural changes, especially technological, which have leaped national frontiers to affect people everywhere.

We will touch briefly on the first two projects, and devote the next chapter to the third.

THE GENERALIST TURNS SPECIALIST

Every intelligent layman should have a working knowledge of the sequence of important events in his own country —including its mistakes as well as its achievements. As there are some ninety sovereign states in the world today, it follows that the generalist is forced to make a digression and specialize.

As a citizen of the United States I should know the broad outlines of the story of North America from Columbus on, especially since the declaration of independence from Britain in 1776. I should know that North America was originally colonized from Asia in the Stone Age, that the Norsemen visited it long before Columbus; and I should take pride in the indigenous civilization of the Maya to the south. All the battles and all the war heroes I do not need to memorize.

A Chinese generalist should know the story from the Shang dynasty on, taking great pride in China as a seminal area in the development of civilization. A generalist from Poland has a rich background to explore; a British generalist looks back to Caesar, if not to Stonehenge; a Russian to the first smelters of iron around the Black Sea.

All generalists in Europe, Australia and the Americas should have a grasp on the sequence of events in Western civilization, from the early Greeks with their affiliates in the Middle East, to the United Nations. Chinese, East Indian and Arabic generalists should have a similar grasp on events in their great areas of civilization. All generalists, East and West, should be aware of the influence of their civilizations one upon another. Diffusion originally flowed from Asia into

Europe, as we have seen; more recently the flow has been reversed.

It is immensely valuable to be acquainted with at least one remote culture, not to answer quiz questions, but for one's personal development and the avoidance of being what anthropologists call "culture-bound." "Those who know no culture but their own, cannot know their own."

Various American universities, including Columbia and Chicago, are now offering broad courses on the great civilizations of the East, though appropriate teaching materials are scarce, and so are qualified instructors.

As a Westerner, suppose you are asked to jot down the impressions that come to you with the word "India." A girl in the University of Chicago produced this list on her first day in such a course:

> white flowing robes
> elephants and cows
> people bathing in muddy rivers
> masses of humanity
> old, gnarled men charming snakes
> women being burned on husbands' funeral pyres.

This young lady went on to do independent research on the Sikhs, and then became a staff assistant in the course on India. The staff includes two anthropologists, two specialists in Sanskrit, one political scientist and one historian. There are similar courses on China and Islam in Chicago, and candidates for B.A. degrees in the social sciences elect one of the three.

We must hope that the idea will spread widely—in Eastern universities as well as Western.

We have opened historical vistas here broad enough to fill another book: What should a generalist know about his own country, his own area of civilization, other great civilizations? We cannot pursue these vistas further, attractive as they may be, but must turn to the spiral of culture as it crosses national lines, affecting all the world's peoples.

12 . The Spiral of Culture

THE WORD "culture" is unfortunate in having at least two meanings. It is commonly used to denote high refinement and works of art. In English, we speak of a "cultured person" as one at home in the literary classics and the symphonies of Beethoven. But as the anthropologists use it, and as we have used it here, culture means the sum total of learned behavior in a given society. It can be divided into three elements:

1. The time-honored customs and skills of the society, of which language is the most important.
2. The accredited beliefs and ideologies of the society, especially its ethics and religion.
3. The man-made constructs or artifacts used by the society —from flint axes to cyclotrons.

There are also levels or rings of culture, both within and without a given society. Some customs—such as the taboos on incest, murder and stealing, division of labor between the sexes, monogamous marriage (often along with other forms)—are universal patterns, found in all known societies.[1] Some patterns have been spread by diffusion, often very widely, but are not universals. One thinks of the plow, the potter's wheel, the sailing ship, the bow and arrow, the

---

[1] In *The Proper Study of Mankind,* I listed thirty-three such universals.

gun, the sewing machine, paper money, the institution of nationalism, the Buddhist religion, and lately jazz music.

Meanwhile, within the society, customs vary with occupation. The code of the British "gentleman," for instance, is limited to a small fraction of British males. Most people today normally belong to a series of culture rings, one inside the next. Your author has been trained to respect the dictates and taboos of at least five major rings, as follows:

Civilization in general, with its habits of eating cereals, living in a house, going to school, paying taxes, respecting the law, using money.

Western civilization, with its science, mathematics, music in the diatonic scale, sovereign states.

Anglo-Saxon culture, with its English language, political democracy, the idea of progress, romantic love as the proper basis for marriage, the masking of one's emotions.

North American culture, with maize, moccasins, canoes, and many words and artifacts from the American Indian; the profound effect of the westward-moving frontier, and the effect of the "melting pot" of many cultures, due to unrestricted immigration up to World War I. The U.S. has also been characterized an "an experiment in transportation."

New England culture, with its nasal twang of speech and devotion to the moral virtues of early rising and keeping busy—Satan always finds mischief for idle hands. A man brought up in New England, talking face to face with a stranger, stands about twenty inches away. If the stranger moves nearer, the New Englander becomes uneasy or even angry. A Latin American, however, feels perfectly comfortable at thirteen inches, and practically out of hearing at twenty. As an office visitor he may climb up on a desk or over a chair to establish his normal proximity.

Your author also has had to learn special words, habits and ceremonies for his professions as accountant, economist, lecturer. His position in the community, depending as it does on achievement, income, accent, education, and so forth, demands a complicated set of customs and haberdashery not shared by all Americans, either higher or lower in the pecking order. A significant thing about the American class system is its flexibility; one can go up or down very rapidly. Not so in Europe; some students call a fluid class structure the outstanding characteristic of America.

TECHNOLOGICAL CHANGE

A culture always resists change, especially institutional change in religion, politics or economics. Technological innovations, if found immediately useful, like television today, will be accepted with less resistance. Technological inventions have the steadiest progress and widest diffusion. Each new discovery establishes a stout platform on which a series of other inventions can be erected. When science enters the picture to discover not just *how* things work but *why* they work the way they do, and then formulates scientific laws, the advance is even faster.

Technology moved very slowly up to the time of the first farmers. We can almost count the basic inventions on our fingers—the use of fire, flint tools, the bow and arrow, clay pots, domestication of the dog, skin clothing, dugout canoes, various devices for counting such as the abacus of the Ishango in Africa, and a few more.

Then inventions came faster. Some animals were domesticated, crops were sown, and cultivation was gradually improved by various devices, including terracing and irrigation, the sickle, the plow. We can guess that as much was invented in a thousand years as in the whole period of prehistory.

With city living and the specialization of tasks, people at last had opportunity to think, concentrate, explore, experiment. In every urban center, ingenious minds began devising innovations, some never to be adopted, others to be taken up by the local community, and then perhaps spread far and wide by diffusion. Organized warfare proved a very rapid agent of diffusion.

Most institutional and social inventions have shown far more erratic curves than technological inventions. Some may be adopted widely, with enthusiasm, but we find fewer solid platforms for further advance. If specialists have read the early record correctly, the political and economic institutions of the city of Ur, 5,500 years ago, do not suffer by comparison with most societies today.

Social innovations are not always helpful, any more than technical ones. But the technical knowledge, for good or evil, goes on expanding, with no sign of retreat. Institutional and social curves show many retreats since Sumeria, and can hardly be called bravely advancing today, as crisis follows crisis.

Why should we find this contrast between two kinds of innovation, both presumably designed to assist Homo sapiens in his dealings with nature and his fellows? I have never found a convincing explanation, but I might hazard a guess. An improved tool or process is clearly visible, with the tangible product it creates, the measurable time it saves, or the power it confers over rivals. But an improved constitution for a nation, for instance, is less easy to visualize. Such inventions too depend more on language and other cultural habits, and so are slower to diffuse. Similarly with works of art, and with some ethical and religious practices. These belong of course in a different category, and generalists will approach them cautiously.

We noted how Egypt and Sumeria invented differing political systems to solve similar problems of city administration. In the scores of known cultures are many varied customs and inventions that deserve wider use, and might greatly enrich the people who would adopt them. Some anthropologists have suggested deliberate study and comparison, deliberate imitation of useful practices, for example in training children, or in techniques of reaching agreement. For the first time in history we have the knowledge and the power to "look over the walls of our own culture," as

Ruth Benedict put it, and admire what we find in others.
But this would involve admitting that we have less than
the whole truth. We readily accept a new drug—quinine or
curare from South American Indians, for example; but a
new custom is something harder to swallow.

A FISTFUL OF INVENTIONS

A catalogue of technological innovations would fill many
books. All I can do here is to suggest the strength and speed
of their spiraling, as they leap cultural boundaries. With
cities, as we have seen, came writing and numerical systems, the priceless zero, the true arch, the sailing ship,
draught animals. Presently five basic mechanical inventions
were developed—the lever, the wedge, the pulley, the
wheel-and-axle and the screw.

Stone Age hunters had used the lever and the wedge for
the transfer of energy, but never worked out the principles
involved. Some early farmers also used the wheel. Egyptians employed the lever thirty-five hundred years ago in
the form of a well sweep called the shadoof, and the wedge
principle, as an inclined plane, was cardinal in building the
pyramids. Roman generals used the lever in siege operations
for lifting armed men to attack high walls. Finally Archi-
medes, the Greek scientist, after perfecting the water screw,
determined the principles of the five basic mechanisms.[2]

PRIME MOVERS

The development of sources of energy, or what engineers
call prime movers, is a fascinating story. The first prime
mover obviously was a man. He learned to aid his muscles
with the lever, the wedge, and later the pulley. The next
prime mover was a beast of burden—ox, horse, llama, or in
some cases the dog. Then came water wheels, windmills and
sails. Hero of Alexandria wrote a treatise on windpower, and
it is possible that the wind was used at an early date in Tibet
to keep prayer wheels in motion.

---

[2] A. P. Usher: *A History of Mechanical Inventions* (McGraw-Hill, 1929).

The most radical invention of the industrial revolution was of course the steam engine, made practicable by James Watt in 1776—an easy date for Americans to remember. It depended upon coal, iron and machine tools capable of shaping a metal cylinder and piston tight enough to hold steam. The steam engine gave rise in turn to the steamboat, the locomotive, to a far more productive if unpleasant factory system, and pumps to make deep mining possible.

The next great prime mover was the internal-combustion engine, which launched the automobile, the truck and the airplane. Today scientists are experimenting with sun engines, the earth pump, atomic power via fission, and perhaps destined to be the most revolutionary prime mover of all, an engine based on the fusion of the hydrogen atom.

PAPER AND PRINTING

Another important item in the spiral of technology was the invention of something cheap and effective to write on. If messages are to be sent and recorded in large societies, they require paper or an equivalent. Clay tablets are too cumbersome, papyrus is too stiff, parchment is much too costly, and the quipu would drive a writer mad. In answer to this demand, the early Chinese invented a linen paper made from flax. The timetable of its diffusion is instructive, for many inventions must have followed a similar rambling course.

First, linen paper spread throughout the Chinese empire up to the Gobi desert. By 750 A.D. it was known in Samarkand, by 800 in Baghdad, by 900 in Egypt, by 1100 in Morocco. The invention crossed to Spain in 1150, reached France in 1200, Italy around 1300, Cologne in 1320, and Nürnberg in 1390—where it was ready for Gutenberg's first printing of the Bible in 1450.[3] Without paper, of what use is a printing press? The Koreans, using wood type, printed on paper long before Gutenberg.

---

3 Following A. P. Usher.

The hand press invented by Gutenberg did not change much for a long time. With Watt's engine came the power-operated press, then the rotary press, and now the modern marvels which have the morning's advertisements in your hands the night before, punctuated here and there with a few sticks of news. Paper and printing in turn stimulated many innovations, not all of them beneficent—books, literacy, public schools, Protestantism (which was made possible by wide Bible reading), pamphleteering, throwaway advertisements, postal systems and the comics.

FASTER AND FASTER

This brings us to the work inaugurated by William F. Ogburn, which well illustrates the spiraling effects of technology, both on further invention and on cultural and social change.[4] He has assembled and plotted a record of inventions, going back in some cases five hundred years. Invariably he found an exponential rate of growth.

This is an awesome rate that grows not by addition but by multiplication. The old story of the farmer and the blacksmith shows its power. The farmer brought his horse to be shod, and asked what it would cost. For the first nail, said the blacksmith, one cent, for the second nail two cents, for the third four cents, and so on. The farmer thought it fair enough. For eight nails in each shoe, or thirty-two nails altogether, the bill came to just $42,949,672.95. If the charge had been on the 1, 2, 3, 4 addition basis, it would have totaled $5.28—which is probably what the farmer had in mind.

Other studies of innovations in chemistry, geology, medicine, over past centuries show similar curves. Even new contributions to economics, education and music follow the general pattern. With each succeeding interval man's creative output has tended to multiply.

The theory behind the graphs is that the more elements of

---

4 See his *Social Change* (Viking Press, revised edition, 1950).

material culture, the greater the number of possible innovations. Three elements can be combined in four different ways, but four elements can be combined in ten different ways, and so on up. Therefore as the number of inventions increases, technological change becomes faster and faster. No other explanation, says Ogburn, can account for the shift from a mud hut on the Euphrates to the skyscrapers of New York in less than 250 generations. Modern builders are no smarter than the ancient villagers; they are just riding an exponential curve.

Technology has forced vast changes in social behavior. An invention causes people to move over, but when they refuse to admit they have moved, the gap between belief and performance widens. Both the shifting and the cultural lag have caused endless trouble. Thus the steam engine produced the "dark Satanic mills," whose employees worked a sixteen-hour day, seven days a week. Business leaders, however, continued to regard factory workers as independent cottage craftsmen, fully capable of looking after all their needs for health, safety, subsistence and steady employment.

Ogburn lists 150 social effects following the invention of the radio, among them:

> Regional differences less pronounced.
> Distinction between classes lessened.
> Concentration on fewer languages.
> Reputation of star athletes inflated.
> Colleges with high scholastic standards put at a disadvantage—publicity going to the big-team colleges.

He lists another 150 effects following the automobile, including a revolution in the art of courtship; 61 effects following the X-ray; 23 following the invention of rayon. It is the business of promoters of new inventions, says Ogburn, to know that social effects are bound to come, and the business of social scientists to predict the repercussions.

No technological inventions have had more stimulating effects than instruments of precision—the compass, the clock, the telescope, microscope, micrometer, the transit, thermometer, barometer, thermostat, and now the Geiger counter, to name a few.

The spiral of culture raises a large question mark over the Great Man theory of progress. This theory assumes that without the lonely giants of the past we would still be living in those Mesopotamian mud huts. But the exponential curves of Ogburn plainly indicate that it is not the giant intellect which determines progress so much as the state of technical advance. Thus when physics reached a certain level of progress in the seventeenth century, and a new kind of mathematics was needed to go forward, both Newton and Leibnitz independently invented the calculus. If neither had lived, the calculus would still have been invented.

The history of science is full of simultaneous inventions of this kind; sometimes three men will produce the same device, unknown to one another. The spiral, not the man, is the determining factor. If Columbus had spent his life ashore in Italy, some other explorer would soon have discovered America. The technology of navigation and shipbuilding allowed a brave captain to sail into the unknown with a fair chance of getting back. This is not to disparage the brave captains—but if brave captains get all the credit for progress, this seriously disparages the human race.

FOUR CONCLUSIONS

The spiral of culture has been only roughly indicated in this chapter, with a handful of cases to illustrate it. But perhaps enough has been said to warrant a few cautious conclusions.

In the first place, the generalist cannot fail to note that the exponential curve of technology is the sturdiest of all cultural advances. Its diffusion is greater and its effects more predictable than in the case of religion, economics, politics and the arts.

In the second place, the generalist cannot fail to be impressed with the way all the world contributes to the spiral. The sailing ship came from Crete, the windmill and iron smelting from the Near East, paper and gunpowder from China, the longbow from England, the cotton gin from America.

The first atomic pile was the result of a long ladder of invention. Here are a very few rungs of the ladder. It goes back to Dalton's atomic theory in 1808, to Mendeleev's Periodic Table in 1869, to J. J. Thompson's discovery of electrons in 1897, to the Curies' finding of radium, with their Nobel prize in 1903, to Rutherford's new model of the atom in 1908, to Bohr's work on electron circuits, to Soddy's discovery of isotopes in 1910, to Urey's heavy-water experiments in 1934, to the work of Einstein, Chadwick, Hahn and Strassmann, Lise Meitner, Frisch, Szilard, and so to Fermi putting the pile in operation under the stadium of the University of Chicago in 1942. Englishmen, Russians, Frenchmen, Danes, Americans, Germans, Italians, as well as scientists from other cultures, combined to make atomic power possible.

The third conclusion for generalists is that technological progress, while steady, is not an unmixed blessing. Waste of natural resources and degradation of human resources have often offset the advance in knowledge. The social sciences have not kept pace with the natural sciences, and innovations, like the steam engine and atomic power, have been loosed on a world unprepared to cope with them. The difficulty is not too much science, but unplanned application.

The fourth and last broad conclusion is that the spiral of culture tends to exert a unifying force. While each society has a culture of its own, as we shall note in more detail in the next chapter, the cultural stream is a world phenomenon and it penetrates every society to a greater or lesser degree. People in all civilized societies today, and some nature peoples as well, use electric power, motor vehicles, telephones, penicillin, cameras, clocks, thermometers, outboard motors. They watch Hollywood and Italian moving pictures, listen to common radio programs, play the latest jazz records, follow the Olympic games, Davis Cup tennis, international chess matches. Increasingly they fly into one another's territory, become familiar with one another's customs, attempt to communicate in one another's language.

Some observers believe that this stepped-up diffusion is gradually establishing a world culture. They say that so many of us are now using so many similar things and accepting so many similar points of view, that we may wake up some day to find that One World is here. To this trend I believe generalists should give every encouragement. If unlimited time were at our disposal, it might well be that the exponential curve would automatically unify mankind. Have we that time?

The result might be a more standardized world or a world, on balance, *less* standardized, through the release of more leisure and more creative intelligence. A world culture might free the human mind as it has never been freed before.

13 . Culture as a Key

WE NOW leave the rough chronology that we have been following in our pursuit of useful knowledge—very rough in the area of written history—to look at some areas of knowledge stored up in the social sciences and humanities. We shall examine the culture concept as a modern tool of social analysis, the lively new disciplines concerned with communication and language, helpful leads from other behavioral sciences, and some economic and political findings not to be overlooked by generalists. We shall then try to give an idea of the cardinal importance of the scientific attitude, and follow it with notes on religion, ethics and art. These constitute prickly territory for generalists from all cultures, but are too vital to neglect.

The spiral of invention we have been sampling has penetrated all societies, and thus encourages a certain amount of world-wide uniformity. Each society of course has combined its borrowings with its indigenous customs to form a unique amalgam. A society may or may not have its own unique language. All North American Eskimos speak a common language, but customs vary sharply from tribe to tribe. The British and American people share English, but only the former have the magnificent display of a royal family, and only the latter the statistical ceremonials of major-league baseball.

Since what is "right" in one society may be quite "wrong"

in another, it is important that the generalist appreciate cultural relativity, with its numerous consequences and applications.[1] He must not forget, however, that all societies are limited by the same biological needs for food, shelter, care of the young. Various philosophers down the ages have appreciated cultural differences and similarities, but only in the last generation has the combined work of many specialists—archaeologists, biologists, linguists, sociologists, social psychologists, and especially cultural anthropologists—given solid scientific support to this key of understanding.

MEXICO AND MISSISSIPPI

Suppose we return to the predicament of Bishop Landa of Mexico in 1550. He ordered, you remember, the destruction of the Maya books—"we burned them all, which they regretted to an amazing degree and caused them affliction." If the bishop had been aware of the culture concept, he would have saved the books, and with them a priceless heritage for mankind. He might have hidden them from his more fanatical followers, but he would have saved them—as the Vatican would undoubtedly order any similar discoveries to be saved today.

Maya and Spaniard were a hemisphere apart. Massachusetts and Mississippi today are states in the same federal union, with the same language and customs, except in the matter of racial segregation. Since the ruling of the Supreme Court in 1954, that public schools should be desegregated "with all deliberate speed," there has been tension, bitterness and violence in the South, sometimes reaching crisis proportions, as in Little Rock, Arkansas, in the fall of 1957.

If one has mastered the culture concept he is in a better position to understand this tragic situation than if he viewed it, like Bishop Landa, solely from his own cultural standards. He comprehends how in the deep South, especially in areas with a heavy ratio of Negroes, the white group holds deseg-

---

[1] The Cross Cultural Survey at Yale University catalogues differences, society by society and custom by custom.

regation to be morally abhorrent—and often quotes the Bible as authority. Most white Southerners believe this sincerely and passionately; they began to believe it soon after they were born, and subsequent experience has reinforced it day by day.

Thus when the Southerner hears a Northerner charge him with defying morality and religion, he concludes that the Northerner is either out of his mind or a potential carpet-bagger, if not a Communist. He may even believe that the Supreme Court is conniving with Moscow. The Southerner is the prisoner of a caste system almost as strong as that of India. India under Prime Minister Nehru has passed laws, too, raising the status of the Untouchables, but the effect so far has been little more successful than in Mississippi.

SOME DO AND SOME DON'T

When American men meet they shake hands; Japanese bow. American church members sometimes pray for rain; Aztec priests used to sacrifice a human being with great ceremony to the same end. "Culture," says Clyde Kluckhohn, "is a set of historically derived regularities in behavior that distinguish one group from another. This central idea explains as much about human behavior as does the idea of gravity in the physical world."

American dentistry is as much concerned with appearance as with checking decay. Our culture demands a mouthful of white, even teeth, as shown in tooth-paste advertisements. Other cultures, such as the Russian, are more concerned with the therapeutic aspect, and do not look down on steel teeth, gold teeth, or an occasional missing tooth. At a rough guess, half the American dental bill is due to cosmetic rather than medical necessity.

In some primitive societies it is still *de rigueur* to lend one's wife to a favored guest. In the days of European chivalry, the *droit du seigneur* allowed the lord of the manor first call on village brides. Shocking as these customs are to us, they were strictly correct in their place and time.

CULTURAL LAG

Culture patterns arise to fill a need, often an essential one. Once incorporated, they may persist long after the need has passed—a phenomenon we have earlier called "cultural lag." Kluckhohn cites two famous examples: first, the convening of the Electoral College to vote for the American President after the election has already been decided by popular vote; and secondly, the ridiculous spelling of many English words. We remember also the "kitchen-midden" people in Denmark, preserving their hunting customs while surrounded by progressive farmers.

Cultural lag in America is responsible for many apparent absurdities, all the way from whip sockets on the dashboards of early automobiles, false smokestacks on Diesel-powered ocean liners, to the years of delay in getting a child-labor law on the statute books. The factory system had changed the environment, but children were still supposed to live in the handicraft age. An English court of law with its wigs and ceremonies manages to do necessary business in a kind of museum of cultural lag. Many current folk sayings in America are also becoming museum pieces, such as:

Buying a pig in a poke.
Locking the barn door after the horse is stolen.
Ground between the millstones.
No more do it than I can fly!
Strike while the iron is hot.

THE EFFICIENCY OF CULTURE

"A social organism," said William James, "is what it is because each member proceeds to his own duty with the trust that other members will simultaneously do theirs . . . all exist on this condition, without which not only is nothing achieved, but nothing is even attempted." In the United States we drive on the right, in Britain on the left. One shudders at the accident rate if we did not automatically anticipate and trust the oncoming driver! We do our duty in the United States by hugging the right-hand shoulder, and simultaneously trust him to do his. Daily life would be unbearably chaotic if everyone were spontaneous in his behavior, driving, walking, speaking, taking things out of shops, as the spirit moved.

Cultural habits also save time by enabling us to perform our customary roles without thinking. If we had unlimited choice in table manners, clothes, family arrangements, money matters, each act would require assessment of facts, a decision, and probably a few false starts. I doubt if even the most extreme Bohemian would last out the day. In tennis, for instance, we consciously decide on our strategy, but the equipment, the scoring and rules of the game are all given. Our skill on the court is built in by long practice. We can decide whether to go to church on a fine Sunday morning or play golf; but once the decision is made, our ceremonial conduct in church, or at the country club, is meticulously prescribed.

The laws of culture are something like those governing the behavior of gas in a container. The scientist can never know what a single molecule of gas will do, but he can accurately predict the behavior of the whole mass under various conditions of temperature and pressure. A social scientist may never know what a single individual will do in a familiar situation, but he can predict what most people will do. He is reasonably sure that no one will get up in church and argue with the minister, and that on the golf course the player who wins the hole always has the "honor" of teeing off. Players violating this code will not long remain on the club roster.

The social scientist knows that most white persons in Alabama and South Africa will oppose desegregation; he knows that most American men of the upper-income groups will rise when a lady enters the room. The laws of culture do not guarantee 100 per cent prediction, but in most social situations they can assure high statistical probability.

Dr. Carleton Coon, the archaeologist, with whom we went

digging in Chapter 7, notes the rigid cultural bonds of his
native workmen in a Syrian cave:

> After luncheon Ubaid would excuse himself very formally,
> take off his shoes, and pray. Then either Saleh the foreman
> or Abu Hasan would start the praying, and all of the older
> and some of the younger men would follow them. Lunching
> and praying yielded a clear picture of the precise pecking
> order of these people. So cut and dried was their system of
> dealing with one another, so entirely formalized their whole
> pattern of living, that each man's behavior was almost com-
> pletely predictable. Subtlety in dealing with them became
> unnecessary. . . .

A good deal of soul-searching goes on currently in the
United States about the "organization man," meaning chiefly
junior executives of large corporations. Their behavior is
said to be severely regimented. What is not sufficiently
pointed out is that all human behavior is severely regimented. Limited as may be the activities of the expectant
tycoon in his office in a New York skyscraper, he is relatively
a free man compared with Saleh and Abu Hasan.

CULTURE AND THE LAW

Formal law, of course, appeared with city living and writing. Only then could rules of conduct already in the culture
be written down and formalized. Nature peoples have no
writing and no complex judicial systems, but their behavior
will usually follow a detailed ritual, with heavy penalties for
infringement. A member may steal once or twice and be ad-
monished and pardoned; the third time he may be speared.
An Eskimo society has no courts or jails, but the elders of
the tribe, acting as judges, may enjoin the death penalty.

Though culture is always slowly changing, laws are often
frozen in the lawbooks, creating a sometimes dangerous lag.
In my state of Connecticut a ferocious series of "blue laws,"
dealing with Sabbath-breaking and other high crimes of
1660, is still on the statute books, and a citizen could legally
be prosecuted for infringing them. The culture concept

throws a strong fresh light on the formal law of any society. Does it synchronize with living customs? If the two are out of step, it may be easier to change the law than the culture. The Prohibition law banning alcoholic beverages in the United States was at war with the culture, and had to be abandoned after a dozen years of bootlegging and violence.

The generalist sees the law of the land not as something unchangeable, but as frozen culture patterns, which need to be surveyed from time to time and modernized.

ON CHANGING A CULTURE

Can leaders deliberately change a culture? We have several revealing examples to study at present. Off hand, one would think it easier to blow up the Andes than to make over the cultural patterns of Germany, Japan, Russia or China. Yet their governments have attempted it. Kluckhohn, studying Russian escapees at the German border in the 1950's, reports that Marxism has produced some cultural changes in persons born after 1920, but observes that "even the most brutal and totalitarian schemes to make a new man meet with stubborn resistance."

In modern Turkey, various repressive decrees against the wearing of veils by women and fezzes by men met with indifferent success. The public schools were then enlisted in the campaign and before long the change was brought about.

Theoretically a culture could be revolutionized in the twenty years it takes for a generation to mature. This assumes, however, that most carriers of the old patterns, especially parents and teachers, have renounced the whole code in order to indoctrinate the new generation—which is impossible.

Every individual not only absorbs his culture; he passes it on with modifications. The creative contribution of most of us is small, but some inspired individuals, like Confucius, Jesus, Mohammed, Gandhi, may be responsible for considerable change. The best analogy is that of the glacier—it moves but you cannot see it move. Even today, when it is traveling faster than ever, we find it hard to measure its rate of change.

Mussolini, Hitler, Lenin, in this century, have wrought political revolutions in their societies, but the day-by-day habits of most Italians, Germans, Russians were not revolutionized. When I was in Russia ten years after the revolution, I was constantly being reminded of classic Russian novels. Railroad travel, office behavior with the use of the abacus and unlimited paper work had been described for me by Tolstoi and Dostoevski. Today, two generations after the revolution, John Gunther reports more changes in behavior, largely due to technology and universal education.

Reformers as well as dictators, unaware of the cultural concept, often try to deflect the glacier without examining either its mass or its rate of flow. Cultures can be changed in small ways deliberately—for instance, by designers of women's fashions—but a substantial change calls for unlimited patience and careful analysis.

DIFFERENCES AND SIMILARITIES

Three important statements can be made about the culture concept. *First,* members of all societies, present and past, have a common "human nature." *Second,* every society has its unique culture, its customs, belief systems, artifacts. *Third,* many patterns in every society have been borrowed from other societies.

The first and the last statements attest similarity, the second attests difference. Initially the differences seem the more important. People say that we must go on disliking, yes, and fighting, because we cannot trust "those foreigners," with their crazy language, their outlandish clothes, and their deplorable moral standards. American soldiers came back from North Africa with this point of view directed at people they called "A-rabs." People in North Africa feel similarly about crazy, hypocritical, sex-mad Americans.

The generalist takes a longer view. He looks again at Edward Steichen's book, *The Family of Man,* with its striking photographs of common human joys and sorrows around the world. Every society is faced with similar problems of food, shelter, love, birth, the rearing of the helpless young, the mastery of language; with work to be done, self-expression to be achieved, faith, illness, death. "The facts of human biology and gregariousness," says Kluckhohn, "supply certain invariant points of reference from which cultural differences take off." The differences are variations on themes arising from our common human nature.

SUMMARY OF THE CULTURE CONCEPT

We have called culture the key to understanding human behavior. What should a generalist keep for ready reference? Here in summary are seven points, developed in the foregoing chapters:

1. An individual without a community is as unthinkable as a community without individuals; man is a social animal. Any attempt to understand him, apart from the society and the culture which contain him, is vain. Psychology floundered in half-truths based on purely individual analysis until this principle was grasped. Theology has trouble at this point too.

2. Without the automatic habits learned through culture, people's behavior would be uncontrollable and unpredictable, and human society unworkable. Suppose you did not know whether the car approaching you at sixty miles an hour would swing right or left?

3. Some patterns are common to all societies, such as taboos on stealing and on murder, within the group. Many patterns are widespread but not universal. Technological innovations tend to spread steadily through all societies, and to follow an exponential curve.

4. Every one of us is culture-bound; it takes practice and concentration to look beyond custom. The generalist *must* look beyond to get a trustworthy view of his own culture.

5. Culture patterns once built in are not easily renounced.

Their persistence after the need has passed is expressed in the term "cultural lag," and the generalist constantly has an eye out for examples.

6. Every individual is both creator and creature of his culture. His contribution may be minute, but combined with others it can bring about slow change. In the calculus of the culture concept, everybody counts.

7. While an analysis of any culture will show lags, absurdities, even lethal patterns (like violent race prejudice, the Indian suttee or suicide of widows, the Aztec blood sacrifice), the course for the long swing is in the direction of survival. Otherwise you and I would not be here.

14 . Language

LANGUAGE is the most important as well as the most complex part of any culture. Indeed, without the ability to tell others about customs, techniques and discoveries, each generation would have to begin afresh, as animals do. The language area happens to be a specialty of your author, who has written two books about semantics and communication, bringing together the work of more accomplished specialists. I will try, however, not to let the following account get out of proportion, but hold firmly to what should interest a generalist about the extraordinary phenomenon of language.

He should know, I think, something about how language works, something about its shortcomings as a communication device, what is being done to remedy these shortcomings, and, in view of the acute problems of the atomic age, what are the chances for a world language.

Let us begin with a statement from a great linguist, Edward Sapir:

> The gift of speech and a well-ordered language are characteristic of every known group of human beings. No tribe has ever been found which is without language, and all statements to the contrary may be dismissed as mere folklore . . . language is an essentially perfect means of expression and communication among every known people. Of all aspects of

143

culture, it is a fair guess that language was first to receive a highly developed form and that its essential perfection is a pre-requisite to the development of culture as a whole.[1]

By "perfection" Sapir means a complete vocabulary and grammatical structure, which enable the speaker to convey his meanings and describe anything of moment in the environment. Sapir does not imply that the various human languages are perfect vehicles for analyzing the outside world; indeed, he thinks many improvements should be made, and is at pains to describe them.

EQUIPMENT AND ORIGINS

The biological equipment for speech is similar for all normal persons of every race. It includes the delicate structures and organs of the mouth, the ears, and special centers in the brain for vocalizing, hearing and associating. No child of course is born with words in his nerve connections, only the machinery to pronounce, store and handle the words later to be learned.

The speech apparatus permits a large range of sound, but has definite limits, for we cannot imitate many cries of birds and other animals, or even hear certain sounds, such as the high notes of a wren. Every language must fall within this range, though each language is built into its speakers by long practice. The speaker of any given tongue will pronounce with ease sounds that are impossible to the unpracticed. A foreign adult, for instance, can never learn the *ng* of Eskimo. Japanese, unless they begin very early, will always have difficulty with the English *l*; Germans with the English *th* sound, and so on.

The sounds in every language, with minor exceptions, are arbitrary and purely synthetic. The languages which children make up on the playground could probably be elaborated to function almost as well. Any sound can be made to stand for any referent, that is, for any physical thing or

---

1 *Culture, Language and Personality* (University of California Press, 1956).

idea. "Kangaroo," for instance, now stands for an Australian animal, and one naturally assumes it is the native label. Not at all. When Captain Cook, the navigator, asked a native for the strange creature's name, the man replied "*Kang-a-roo*," meaning "I don't know." A few words do imitate actual events, such as "boom," "buzz," "crack," in English. But most words in all languages are made up of whole cloth.

If true man appeared only with language, as we earlier theorized, it is conceivable that he began his career with a very simple vocabulary. It would be fascinating to know how he fitted these original sounds to meanings. There must have been a good deal of pointing and experimenting, perhaps disagreements and quarrels as to the best sound to represent "water," or "bear." Hunting bands which migrated would take the primeval language with them, but a new environment would call for new words, and gradually a whole new language might evolve. Linguists estimate that it requires some five thousand years completely to divorce a new language from an old.

If you and I were wrecked on a desert island, and you spoke only English and I only Arabic, and we were both too stubborn to learn the other's language, we could invent a language for ourselves. We could call water "wap," air "wip," sand "wop," and coconuts "wup," and work from nouns to verbs to adjectives, and finally to an ordered grammar—if we continued to be stubborn, and had plenty of time on our hands.

NO PRIMITIVE LANGUAGES

Before Alfred Russel Wallace, many students believed that "savages" spoke in grunts and squeals like beasts. Such people had so few words, it was thought, that they had to supplement them with gestures, and so could not talk in the dark. The Hottentot language was supposed to consist largely of apelike cries. Pure theory, for no white man had listened to it carefully.

When trained linguists began to study the speech of

nature peoples they soon realized that "savages" possessed language systems as sophisticated in structure as any "civilized" tribe. Nature peoples had the same vocal apparatus and brain area, and they put it to equally intricate use in describing what they saw and felt.

Every language, no matter how strange it may sound to the uninitiated, is highly systematized—giving us another similarity in the family of man. Linguists collecting the virgin tongue of some band of head-hunters in New Guinea can soon analyze its phonetic structure. The raw data of all languages are so extremely formal that linguistics is considered the most exact of the social sciences. *Linguists have never found a language which by any stretch of the imagination can be called primitive.*

The language of any community is suited of course to its special interests. English is better for talking about motorcars; Arabic is better for talking about camels—having six thousand words devoted to the performance of that improbable animal.[2] Eskimo is better for dealing with snow and ice —and perhaps should be taken up by skiers and mountain climbers. All tongues in their complexity bear an exact relation to the complexity of the brain.

Benjamin Lee Whorf shows clearly how the view of space and time implicit in the language structure of Hopi Indians is closer to Einstein's concept of relativity than is the view implicit in any Indo-European tongue.

OVERTONES AND TRANSLATIONS

Once a language is in use, however accidental its origins, it grows and develops like a living organism. It becomes second nature to generation after generation, and acquires overtones and special associations with childhood memories and past experiences. In civilized cultures a written literature arises, whose classic works of poetry and prose express profound meanings and delicate nuances. Such associations

---

2 A camel, somebody has said, "looks as if it had been designed by a committee."

and the passage of time clothe certain words with deep emotional significance.

As language, like other elements in the culture, is always slowly changing, there is no "correct usage" in the absolute sense. The generalist realizes that other societies feel as much devotion to their particular sound sequences as he does to his own, and that their classics will lack certain associations for him, and vice versa. The best translations will be those which use local overtones with sympathy and discrimination.

Poetry, Robert Frost once observed, is what gets lost in translation. And Jean Cocteau, reviewing Baudelaire, is fully aware of translation difficulties when he says:

"Baudelaire's prose, like Montaigne's, is one of the most admirable in the world. It is unfortunately untranslatable because, like all beautiful prose, it depends on inner rhythms, syncopations, sound-waves and verbal clusters indigenous to the language in which the sentences are written."

Those who try to preserve strict purity of language are on very debatable ground. People with accents and dialects differing from our own are not necessarily debasing the coin of language, but may indeed be opening up rich new mines. The major languages themselves have admitted various dialects, as new speakers crossed over sea or mountain range from a strange environment.

The real charge against a particular usage is that order has been violated and meaning thereby lost. Words can change their meanings gradually, but if grammatical structure is too badly abused the communication line is broken, and the primary function of language destroyed. A good deal of modern English verse, as well as some of the prose of James Joyce, hovers on this brink. Such poets will not thank me, but it sometimes seems that they understand neither the structure, the function nor the importance of the language they write.

THE ONE–PROPER–MEANING SUPERSTITION

The 500 most used words in English have been analyzed and found to possess 14,070 separate meanings, or an average of 28 meanings per word.[3] This piece of research disposes once and for all of a common fallacy: that any given term has only one proper meaning. Most words have a variety of meanings, depending on context. If a speaker remarks, for instance, that Los Angeles is a "great town for a scientist," the hearer must determine whether he means Ph.D.'s or Christian Scientists.

Meanings also change through time. When James II observed that St. Paul's Cathedral in London, newly completed by Sir Christopher Wren, was AMUSING, AWFUL and ARTIFICIAL, hearers of that period understood that he meant PLEASING, AWE-INSPIRING and SKILLFULLY ACHIEVED. Earlier, when Francis Bacon referred to persons as INDIFFERENT, OBNOXIOUS and OFFICIOUS, he meant, in the usage of today, IMPARTIAL, SUBMISSIVE and READY TO SERVE—a very different character indeed![4]

LEARNING TO TALK

Animals lack the intricate human apparatus for speech, and the even more intricate and mysterious brain connections. Various experiments in raising bright chimpanzees with children of the same age show an approximately equal development until the child begins to talk. Then he gains rapidly on the poor ape, who can be taught to mumble "mama" but little else.

Here is a maze, described by Norman L. Munn, in which the subject has to figure out a correct sequence of turning— twice to the right, then twice to the left, with no clues to help.[5] A rat fails completely even after two thousand runs. Cat and raccoon may solve it in from five hundred to eight hundred runs; a chimpanzee in around a hundred runs. Now

3 Charles C. Fries, quoted by Irving Lee in *How to Talk with People*, Harper, 1952.

4 Simeon Potter, *Our Language*, Penguin Books, 1950.

5 *Scientific American*, June, 1957.

observe: An adult human being, after a few trips around the maze to catch on, will say: "Oh, I get it. I'm supposed to go *twice* to the right and *twice* to the left." Speaking brings the solution. A child under three, however, is about on a par with a chimpanzee; "children do not surpass animals on the test until they begin to verbalize it."

By the time the normal child is six years old, the linguists say, he can manage the structure of his native tongue. He will need to learn many more words, many details about how words behave; but he is in fair command of the fundamentals. Take, for instance, the three English words: DEER, MAN, SHOOT. By the age of six, the child knows that placed in the order: MAN SHOOTS DEER, the words make sense. In the order SHOOTS DEER MAN, they make no sense; while the order DEER SHOOTS MAN conveys only what might happen in a fairy story.

SPEAKING AND WRITING

The child uses his comprehension of structure not only to make his needs understood, but also to think about his own experiences. "Thought," says Sapir, "is hardly possible without the symbolic organization brought by language"—and for systematic thinking, the language must be written down. Talking came eons ago, writing just the other day. All normal children teach themselves to talk by imitating their elders and they work hard at it. But many children have trouble with reading and writing—perhaps because the business is so recent, perhaps because it is badly taught, perhaps both.

Speaking is a richer experience than reading. It adds gestures, accents, pauses, dynamic movement to the words. Linguists are developing a specialty called "kinesics" to analyze this enrichment of speech. Your true linguist is a little superior about writing, considering it a pale symbolization of a symbolization. Compared to a live enthusiastic speaker pounding the desk, a page of type seems to him anemic stuff.

Writing, however, has one great virtue; it stays put. No-

body (unless he has total recall) can remember exactly
what he heard even an hour later, as any judge can bear
witness. But what Confucius said thousands of years ago
is there on the page exactly as his scribes wrote it. Civilization, as we have repeatedly noted, would not be manage-
able without written messages. Today spoken words can be
preserved by various techniques of recording, and many
new uses are being developed for these techniques. Some
are making their way into the courtroom as evidence.

COMMUNICATION FAILURES

We not only take for granted the common marvels of
language, but we may credit language with a precision far
beyond its actual performance. Despite the child's early
grasp of the structure of language, his road to understanding
is beset with pitfalls and barricades, some of them imposed
by the nature of language, others by distortions in its use. To
perceive these roadblocks we must turn to the young discipline of semantics, which has been defined as *the systematic
study of meaning.*

We can divide meaning into two grand categories: the
literal meaning of the speaker's (or writer's) words, and
his intention—what he really means. Sometimes his real
meaning belies his words, as when the phrase "How nice to
see you" conceals the thought, "Of all the rotten luck to
have *you* turn up!" The first category is concerned with
straight communication, the second with its intentional use
for gaining power, through various kinds of so-called double
talk, such as advertising, propaganda drives and political
oratory.

Semanticists identify barriers in both categories. An outstanding example of the first kind is:

The confusion of words with things, or word magic. Many
linguistic patterns, says Sapir, "make the word do duty for
the thing . . . as the ultimate unit of reality." Thus Plato
solidified "the Good" into such an ultimate unit. Search as
you will with telescope, microscope, radar and Geiger

counter, you will not find anything to correspond to "the Good." You can find good water, good fields of corn, good acts by individuals or groups—plenty of events to be called "good," but not the abstraction itself. Superstitions, witchcraft, demonology are often the result of making the word do duty for the thing.

Because a word is there, we often assume that a definite thing must be behind it. When you hear the word "Communism" what do you see? As a practicing generalist you should see nothing at all; but many people see a foul shape moving to engulf the world. Without a firm realization that words are not things, it is easy to stock one's environment with a zoo of imaginary entities, essences, "isms," "ologies" and other formidable spooks.

A bare list of other semantic blocks includes:

Spurious identification, including the well-known form of guilt-by-association.

The wholesale application of two-valued logic: "Those who are not with us are against us" is an example which can do great damage to a realistic foreign policy, by forcing neutral nations into *either* the capitalist *or* the Communist camp.

Failure to find the referent for abstract terms. Thus when A speaks of "democracy" he means the right to vote, while to B the word means belonging to a union. Their minds do not meet, and however loudly they shout they cannot understand each other.

Confusing facts with inferences or opinions—well exemplified by the anecdote of the lawyer who told the jury: "These, gentlemen, are the conclusions upon which I base my facts!"

Gobbledygook. Prolixity and obscurity; drowning meaning in technical terms. Very common in large bureaucratic establishments, and not unknown in academic groves. Useful to cover a vacuum in knowledge.

Failure to allow for cultural differences. Delegates to the

United Nations face this barrier every day. The culture concept and communication theory meet at this point—as they do at many others.

Failure to appraise the speaker's background and motives. What are his goals, and how do they affect his talk? (This illustrates the second or power-drive kind of meaning.)

MATHEMATICAL LANGUAGES

Ordinary language, as observed earlier, is not always adequate for acquiring new knowledge in the sciences. New languages have been invented, which give more precision; also they do not have to be translated. $E = mc^2$ is intercultural and universal.

Let us follow Anatol Rapoport as he explains the advantages of thinking in mathematical symbols.[6] Most sciences, he says, are defined by their subject matter, but mathematics is defined by its method. It has no subject matter, and its chief tool is a blackboard. Doing sums is not regarded as mathematics in the modern sense; we have all heard of some great mathematician who cannot balance his checkbook. What he can do is to apply rigorous logic to the manipulation of symbols, and so perceive significant relations—an ability that requires a high degree of mental maturity. After the abstract relations have been established, the mathematician may call for the laboratory men to test their application.

Rapoport gives us an illuminating example of mathematical thinking. Here is a small boy with one brother. You ask him if he has a brother and he says yes. Then you ask him if his brother has a brother, and almost certainly he will say no. Only later will he understand that "brother" in this context is a *relationship,* not a person. Many relations in the physical world can be translated into a mathematical picture to which rigorous logic can be applied. The results can then be transferred back into new conclusions about the physical world.

[6] In *Frontiers of Knowledge.*

Any school child will laugh if you try to make him believe that 3 plus 3 equals 7, but you can often make him believe the grossest fallacies symbolized in words. A generalist as such is not required to be a mathematician—though it will certainly do him no harm—but he should be aware of the limitations of ordinary language. He should realize the great advantage specialists have today over investigators of the prescientific age, whose thinking was mostly verbal. The Greeks and Romans had geometry, but no algebra, no zero, no calculus or probability theory. Much knowledge was thus closed to them, for they had no way to talk about it.

THE COMMUNICATION SCIENCES

Not only the mathematicians and the semanticists are pushing ahead on the communication front, but so are other disciplines, including both theory and application.

Cybernetics is one such science; it has produced the electronic computer, which in turn is producing automation, and what some engineers call the "second industrial revolution."

Linguistics is advancing into kinesics and metalinguistics. The latter studies ways in which language influences the speaker's world view.

Perception theory tries to show how past experience shapes our comprehension of what we perceive now.

How children learn to talk is being intensively studied, also *how animals communicate*. Specialists assure us that parrot talk is not talk at all, only an imitation of sounds. A parrot has no proper language centers in his brain.

Listening theory is advancing but hardly fast enough, in view of the fact that listening is the other half of talking.

Meanwhile communication studies are helping to solve labor-management problems, aiding decision making by business executives, and reducing misunderstanding in face-to-face groups of all kinds—classrooms, board meetings, labor-union meetings, international meetings, school committees. As a member of the planning commission in my town, I try to use the new findings when dealing with fellow members, with other officials of the town government, and in public relations with citizens generally. Each group presents a continuing communication problem.

There is useful knowledge here for the generalist to use in his next meeting, indeed in every meeting he attends.

NOTES ON A WORLD LANGUAGE

A Gallup poll in 1953 asked adults in Finland, Canada, Norway, Holland, the United States: "Should school children be taught an international language?" Citizens of five countries answered overwhelmingly in the affirmative. Today, as international problems mount, one suspects the ratio would be even higher. (The children, however, were not polled.)

A number of international communication systems are already in vigorous use, in addition to Arabic numbers and the mathematical symbols already mentioned. Botanical terms, chemical formulas, the metric system, musical scoring, navigational symbols are some of them. A UN agency did some work on traffic symbols, uniform for the world's highways. At various periods in the past, Church Latin, Arabic, Greek, French, English have served as auxiliary languages. Latin was the common language of scholars for centuries, and one may still find it on his college diploma.

Though language as a cultural phenomenon is universal, there is no universal language. Dr. George Trager estimates that about twenty-five hundred tongues are spoken in the world today, not counting dialects. Nine of them, in this order—English, Russian, North Chinese, Spanish, German, Japanese, Hindustani, French, Italian—combine to serve more than half the people of the world. Many native tongues, Dr. Trager mournfully observes, are rapidly becoming extinct—like the whooping crane. The languages are as unique and irreplaceable as the birds, and far more significant—indeed priceless to scholars. Linguists would like to send expeditions into the world's backwaters to collect all these vanishing tongues before it is too late.

There is popular support for a world language to be taught as an auxiliary in the schools, and there is increasing need for it. It makes sense, and is bound to come—but not tomorrow. Despite its logical advantages there are formidable questions involved.

Should it be one of the nine leaders in the above list— say English—or a new, synthetic language? Logically, Basic English would be the easiest to adopt, because so many of the world's people already use English in one way or another. But can you picture the debate in the Assembly of the United Nations over the official adoption of English, or Russian, or any other existing tongue? Speakers of all other languages would unite solidly against it.

If a synthetic, should it be a language already worked out, like Esperanto, Volapük, Interlingua, or a brand-new design? The above three are based on Greek and Latin roots, and might not be acceptable to the great civilizations of the East.

If a brand-new synthetic were to be established, who should design it, and on what principles? How would it be publicized and introduced? Such questions are not to be answered overnight. Some day, after its highway symbols have been accepted, the UN might summon a group of linguists, mathematicians, semanticists, anthropologists, and go to work on a synthetic acceptable to all the world.

Sapir believed that the chosen auxiliary should be completely foreign to everybody, in the interest of peace and harmony. For a time, he thought, it would be purely cold and synthetic, but after two or three generations a literature with overtones might develop. Ultimately it might become as rich as any natural language, while if carefully designed, it could eliminate many of the roadblocks and confusions built into the former—"as superior to any accepted language as the mathematical method of expressing quantities and relations is superior to the more lumbering methods of expressing these questions in verbal form."

Some kind of international language we must have eventually, and if enough attention were devoted to its design, it could be a far more efficient language than any of the twenty-five hundred now in use. Whether the Shakespeares and Dantes and Tolstois of the future will use it is problematical, despite Sapir's optimism. Language is a function of culture, and a world culture—not merely a world planning center, or a world police force—is a long way in the future.

15 . Some Studies of Behavior

THE INTELLIGENT layman is interested not only in the role of language in reducing world tensions; he also wants to know what knowledge is available to promote negotiation and accommodation between the great powers. This is a question in the area of the behavioral sciences.

He wants to understand too what can be done to lessen tension between the races, and between worker and employer, and how to improve community relations. He would especially like to understand himself better, and why he often has so much trouble doing what he thinks he ought to do, and how he can get on more happily with his family, and in his personal relations generally.

Aside from these rather practical motives, a good generalist possesses a healthy curiosity. So far in this book he has viewed Homo sapiens from the outside, at a considerable distance, as a part of the astonishing life of the planet, and has noted various mysteries. How and where this creature originally developed, how he survived as a hunter for many thousands of years, as a farmer and city dweller for a few more thousands; the purpose of his excess brain capacity even beyond what he needs for the intricate skills of language—these are some of the mysteries. The study of various cultures (where indeed the behavioral sciences begin) answers some questions but raises others: for example, which

traits are common to man of every age and place, which
are unique in a given society or even individual; why can
the same complex customs arise independently in widely
separate cultures?

The generalist views Homo sapiens however not only
from without, but, as a member of the species, from within.
His own experiences are often as perplexing as the mysteries
of written history and prehistory. Many critics today insist
that these mysteries are insoluble, and that there is something impious in even attempting to understand them. The
same critics may turn around and complain that the social
sciences are vague, theoretic, without objective proof or
practical utility. Other students think that the difficulty is
akin to a mechanical puzzle, complex but not insoluble,
which when worked out will permit the specialist to predict
future behavior with great precision.

A FEW LANDMARKS

The latter mechanical view was held, for example, by
Wilhelm Wundt, who set up the first laboratory for the
study of behavior at Leipzig in 1879, and it has had great
influence on several generations of followers. The first scientific study of normal children, from a very different frame of
reference, was made at the Child Welfare Research Station
in Iowa in 1916. William James at Harvard in the 1890's
was one of the fathers of modern psychology, but it was
Sigmund Freud and his followers who, with psychoanalysis,
made an objective view of behavior common coin throughout the world. Poets, novelists, playwrights, as well as doctors, social workers and after-dinner conversationalists, became excited about complexes, conditioning, inferiorities,
and the interpretation of dreams. Academic studies also
grew rapidly during this period, and attempted from various
angles to collect exact knowledge about human behavior.
Among the disciplines now involved are individual and
social psychology, psychiatry, psychosomatic medicine, sociology, group analysis and group therapy, aptitude testing,

public-opinion research. Studies of economic behavior and political behavior also fall under this general head, to be developed in later chapters.

The findings of the behavioral sciences are not universally welcomed—as witnessed by the opposition to the Kinsey reports on sexual behavior—but people do crave information which they can use to order their lives. We recall the popularity of Dorsey's *Why We Behave Like Human Beings,* and Overstreet's *The Mature Mind.*

Psychology is easily the most discussed of all the social sciences, more on the public mind than economics, its nearest rival. "I used psychology on the boss and got transferred." The term is blithely used by big-time baseball players, prize fighters, door-to-door salesmen, taxi drivers, labor leaders, as well as college graduates, along with popular tags and phrases—"Bad case of Oedipus." . . . "He's got an inferiority complex." . . . "Too much unsound speculative psychology in the stock market."

More than half the members of the American Psychological Association are now outside the universities, acting as professional consultants and researchers for industry, government, airlines, schools, private clients. Industrial psychology is particularly active. The Standard Oil Company of New Jersey, for instance, retains psychologists to help prepare employees for that Day of Judgment when they must leave the company at sixty-five. Without preparation, experience shows that many employees will crack up.

A number of schools and colleges provide counseling service for students worried about their grades, their sex life, or other personal problems. By and large, psychologists give advice to normal people, or people who are only normally upset, while psychiatrists, with medical degrees, take charge of the more seriously disturbed. The tensions of modern living are producing gigantic problems in mental illness, greater than the present corps of psychiatrists can handle, either in Europe or America.

Generalists can hardly expect to follow all the research on the behavioral front. Even specialists need information clearing houses, and such publications as *Psychological Abstracts*. Generalists should be aware, however, of the wide scope of the activity, and aware of some of the great advances in the social sciences that came during World War II.

Money did not matter in wartime, and one outstanding achievement after another resulted—aptitude testing for airmen; "area studies" in the Pacific, preliminary to storming the beaches; the control of inflation by all major belligerents for the first time in military history. To dismiss this brilliant work as the stuff of theorists and dreamers is to betray an ignorance of which no generalist should be guilty. Applied social science saved thousands of lives and billions of dollars; it appreciably shortened the war.

THE FREQUENCY DISTRIBUTION CURVE

We will devote the rest of this chapter to a few findings in behavioral science useful to generalists, who can use many of them in day-to-day living, as I myself try to do.

Few things are more important than understanding the people one encounters, and science has some aid for us here. Finding villains is less easy than it used to be. Formerly, action was the test; a bad act was held to prove the actor inherently bad; a few bad acts by members of an alien group indicated a bad nation or a bad class. It was very simple: "All labor unions are good, or bad"; "all Russians are good, or bad." If a person one met belonged to one or another of these categories, he was ticketed in advance, regardless of his actions.

No sensible and tolerant person can permit himself such ready-made evaluations. A simple remedy is the frequency distribution curve, used by biologists and social scientists, with saints at one end, sinners at the other, and the rest of us in between.

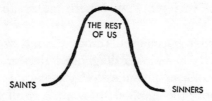

Social scientists draw these curves for every human characteristic which is measurable. Everyone differs slightly from everyone else, even in traits which cannot be measured, and he places somewhere on the great arc. Only those at the far ends can be judged as very tall or very short, or very fat or very thin, or very bad or very good, or very clever or very stupid—on say an IQ test. The distribution concept can be used like a powerful steam hammer to break up the monolithic blocks of prejudice and two-valued appraisal, where everything is classified as either black or white.

Having exonerated or identified a "bad" person, one may move to another level of evaluation. Granted he has committed a crime, what made him do it? Here the psychiatrists and psychologists inquire about his motivations, perhaps beginning with a study of his early family life, his relations with his mother, his emotional security, environment, street gangs, schooling, income, major frustrations. The effects of culture and subcultures will be assessed. Though specialists may not agree that "to know all is to forgive all," they will want to know a great deal more than just what happened in the few moments when the crime was committed. They have a mystery to unravel far more profound than that faced by the detectives, whipping out microscopes for fingerprints.

We come then to a final level of behavior analysis: Can our bad man be cured of his "badness"? Shall he be temporarily removed from society, given a new environment, shock treatment, group therapy, brain surgery? Is he so far gone that the death penalty is the only solution, for the well-being of society? Few experts advocate this for any case.

The behavior specialists, through some such procedure as the above, can help to diagnose behavior problems for individuals, such as juvenile delinquents, for instance, and can even apply the method to groups, small or large. The German people, for example, were abnormally frustrated by the terms of the Treaty of Versailles. (Whether they should have been is another question; they were.) Their frustration and blocked goals more than anything else accounted for the rise of Hitler. The past life of Hitler, in turn, opens a further fascinating study.

Such analysis of past experience emphasizes a unifying element in behavior research. We are confronted with a problem; what is the sequence of events leading up to it? It will probably be a matter of process, rather than simple cause and effect. I should like to comment briefly on five areas of behavior research concerned in varying degrees with past experience.

1. The analysis of psychological conditioning
2. Perception theory—how we know things
3. The frustration-aggression cycle
4. Psychosomatic analysis
5. Needs and wants

CONDITIONING

All of us come to a situation not freshly, but as molded by the culture and by individual experience. Pavlov could condition a dog to drool at the sound of a bell, after it had associated the bell with food. People may come to connect quite unrelated events that have accompanied certain rewards or punishments. This process is widely used in education and learning, and it also helps to explain much behavior that otherwise may seem irrational. What a person does in a given situation is largely the result of a long sequence of situations in the past.

Clinically such questions are usually referred to a psychiatrist or psychoanalyst. The psychoanalyst, notebook in hand beside the patient's couch—a scene which has become standard with cartoonists—tries to help the patient locate some event in earlier life now covered by feelings of guilt or shame. Once brought back into consciousness, the experience should cease to trouble the patient, who, it is hoped, will tackle life with renewed vigor. Sometimes indeed he does. One serious difficulty with psychoanalysis is the cost, for it is a strictly handicraft operation. The problem of mental illness, with millions of sufferers, demands a therapy based on public health and mass production. Experiments were made along this line with so-called "shell-shocked" cases in the war, and are being made now in group therapy.[1]

The generalist can become aware of past conditioning in himself, as well as in others. What buried experiences of childhood, what abnormal attachments, what searing sounds and sights are affecting his behavior at the present moment? What judgments are called for, in the light of these experiences?

PERCEPTION THEORY

A recent school of behavior is studying in detail how we perceive things. The theory, backed by extensive laboratory data, holds that the way we perceive any object, as well as the significance we give to an event, is heavily influenced by past experience. Thus two crossed sticks burning in a field may mean a marshmallow-toasting party to A, a gratifying symbol of white supremacy to B, the threat of a grass fire to C, and the terror of lynching to D.

The theory connects with what I like to call the "thingumbob principle," citing William James. A tiny water creature, says James, sees a shape swimming beside it and exclaims: "Hullo, Thingumbob again!" It has had experience with thingumbobs, and knows whether to stay or flee. It

1 Both described in my *Power of Words*. See work of Douglas Kelley and Carl Rogers.

follows that an organism does well to collect many varied
thingumbobs, in the interest of understanding and survival.
It follows, too, that a person may fail to learn from books
because he has not accumulated the thingumbobs to which
the words in the book refer.

The psychology of the future, says Hadley Cantril, will
investigate present behavior and experience as a *transaction,*
action across, including the effects of the past and expecta-
tions of the future. Perception is never absolute, but rather
a matter of probability; we *bet* that this is a chair, or a gun,
or a lovers' quarrel, based on our past experience. "We build
up constancies and begin to count on them."

Perception theory can take us into pretty deep technical
waters; but the generalist can readily grasp the central idea
and add it to his stock of useful knowledge. What he sees
out there is not exactly what his wife or his neighbor sees.
It is probably very different from what an Eskimo sees—
depending on the experiences stored away in the minds of
each.

FRUSTRATION-AGGRESSION

The past here tends to be fairly close to the act. You are
driving, let us say, along a narrow two-lane highway with
many curves, late for an appointment, when you are
blocked by a slow-moving truck. Mile after mile it crawls
along, increasing your frustration. Finally you can tolerate
it no longer; you step on the accelerator, swing out in the
opposite lane and take a chance. What driver has not felt
this impulse, and how many thousands of accidents has it
caused? It illustrates the so-called frustration-aggression
cycle, which social scientists have documented in a small
classic.[2]

To be alive, these scientists say, is to have goals of various intensities, things we want to achieve, from making an
appointment, to making a million, to marrying the girl.

---

2 John Dollard, Leonard Doob and others: *Frustration and Aggression*
(Yale University Press, 1939).

Something or somebody blocks the goal. Frustration gathers and grows, until internal pressure bursts into external action. The action can take various forms: direct, against the source of blockage; indirect, against the family dog, or a cabinet loaded with expensive china, or an innocent bystander. The pressure may find release in spreading malicious rumors, or at the extreme, in suicide.

A man rushed out of his house in Brooklyn and punched a passing stranger on the nose. He told the judge he couldn't help himself, he had been quarreling with his wife, he couldn't hit her, and had to take it out on somebody. It was his bad luck that the stranger happened to be a police detective. American soldiers, drafted for World War II, were badly frustrated by the unwonted discipline of army life. They took it out on their officers—mostly verbally. On entering combat, however, they could take it out on the enemy. From then on their officers were more highly regarded.

Children are continually frustrated as they are broken in to the culture, minding their manners, keeping quiet, washing their faces, picking things up, going to school—all sorts of disciplines which constrain their freedoms. If parents are unaware of this and let the frustrations become extreme, the outcome may be disastrous—anywhere from juvenile delinquency to a bad temper throughout life.

A generalist in the range of an aggressive outburst had better dodge. While he takes cover, however, his thought should not be "What an awful person!" so much as "What's eating him?" What blocked goals motivate this most unpleasant behavior? To locate the blockage and remove it is the ultimate solution, but if this is impossible, the person might find a harmless outlet for aggression: splinter the pins in a bowling alley, for instance, or cut down a tree, or climb a mountain.

PSYCHOSOMATIC INTERRELATIONS

This study is at once quite new and very ancient. It is based on the premise that one's bodily processes are closely linked to one's mental processes; experience on either side affects the other. Physicians have been aware of this back to the Greeks; theologians have incorporated it into the practice of praying for recovery, Christian Science is built upon it, Yogis and medicine men draw heavily on it. Intelligent persons down the ages have reminded themselves that the extremely gloomy view of the world they may take in the early morning can have a close connection with what they ate or drank the night before. *Per contra,* they may realize that ulcers of the stomach and other painful lesions often follow worry and tension.

It is rarely possible to find a direct cause-and-effect relation in these conditions. Most of them are better viewed as *processes,* with interaction in both directions. I once heard a brilliant psychiatrist, the late Dr. Douglas Kelley, clearly demonstrate how a physical symptom produces anxiety, which makes the symptom worse, and so round and round in a vicious circle.

Recent findings and experience with new drugs tend to emphasize the somatic side of the balance. Correlations have been found between "mental" illness, including schizophrenia, and certain conditions that can be chemically tested and treated. The complex and delicate work of enzymes and hormones and the intricate constituents of blood plasma would seem almost beyond analysis, but the biochemists keep refining their tools and tests and their conclusions as well. We should follow their work and try to understand it, with suitable reservations when it is sensationally reported. There is still a long way to go but current progress is remarkable.

Formal medicine, we recall, until quite recently assigned one group of practitioners to ailments of the body, and a smaller group to ailments of the mind. Today no doctor in his senses believes that there is a clean-cut distinction. I have yet to meet a competent general practitioner who has not a flair for psychiatry, or who will not admit that a large share of his practice lies in calming down his patients' fears and forebodings. Some doctors say mental stress can cause almost any known disease, and make an individual accident-prone. A realistic approach must consider the total organism—with frequent reference to the pressures of culture.

WANTS AND NEEDS

Moralists are concerned with what people ought to want, social scientists with what they in fact do want. This has great political importance as well, and leaders can draft better policies if mass wants built out of experience are identified, their strength appraised and effects anticipated. (A Hitler can draft worse ones.)

A group of scientists, led by Dr. Mark A. May, in 1953 made a careful analysis based on data from the U.S. Information Service. They identified seven major wants shared by most of the world at the time. People everywhere, the May report concluded:

Want peace. It is a universal desire in all countries.

They want political independence; no more colonialism, no more foreign masters.

They want to maintain their own traditional culture, customs and religious beliefs.

They want the facts, the truth about domestic and foreign affairs. They have become dissatisfied with the news they have been getting.

They want to know more about other countries and their peoples; they would like to go and see at first hand.

They are tired of low living standards, and want better ones, more economic security.

They want to be on the winning side.

The people of the world on this showing are oriented toward survival, but their leaders, one fears, have less simple goals.

The concept of wants is useful in evaluating almost any

large problem that involves many people. It helps us to understand the massive popularity of Stalin, Mussolini and Hitler, on the one hand, and the popularity of Churchill, Roosevelt and Eisenhower, on the other. The usual explanation runs in terms of a leader's personal characteristics, but a better explanation, scientists say, is often that the leader is able to symbolize a mass want. Once he can do this, any action he takes is not only right but inspired. His followers accept him as a "father image," which satisfies their deep emotional needs, and which they will give up reluctantly, if at all. The actual person may have little relation to the imagined person. When puzzled by the popularity of demagogues, one remembers that people do not see the demagogy; they are blinded by their own need.

ANALYSIS OF GROUPS

Another area in the study of behavior is expanding at practically an exponential rate—the analysis of face-to-face groups.

Why does one committee solve a problem in an hour, and another take days and weeks on a similar problem? How do the Quakers in their business meetings arrive at unanimous agreement—as they have been doing for three hundred years? What kind of leadership is best in what situations? How can change be fairly and wisely introduced? What can be done to make PTA meetings, classrooms, directors' meetings, labor-union meetings, to say nothing of United Nations meetings, more effective?

Such studies are sometimes called "group dynamics." A pioneer was the late Kurt Lewin, a German Gestalt psychologist with a talent for devising experimental techniques which did not copy the laboratory method of chemistry and physics. His work is being energetically carried on by the so-called Bethel school. Though group dynamics is still in its infancy, it has had a wide press, and some principles are emerging not to be overlooked by generalists.

Among them are these five rules for making face-to-face groups more effective:

Encourage maximum participation by all members.

Practice democratic rather than autocratic leadership. (The technical term is "permissive" leadership.)

Keep communication lines open. If a row develops, get back rapidly to the facts and avoid heated opinions.

Protect the emotional security of others. Never let a member feel ridiculous.

Practice better listening. Identify yourself with other members rather than play a lone hand. Expect to learn from other members, and in some cases expect a group decision to be wiser than that of any individual. (As often happens with the Quakers.)

Specialists in group dynamics encourage a technique they call "role-playing," where one learns, through an un-rehearsed charade, to put himself in another person's place. An official of the Rubber Workers once told me how his union had role-played the meeting before negotiating its annual contract with the employer group. Some of the union negotiators, including my friend, took the part of actual company officials, while others continued to be union men. Important points in the coming negotiations were acted out with spirit. "You know," he said, "it wasn't long before I could feel those stockholders breathing down my neck!"

If officials of the U.S. State Department would role-play the Russian Presidium from time to time, they might begin to understand how it feels to be surrounded with hostile bases, armed and able to destroy one's cities in a few minutes' flying time. If the Party Presidium would role-play the U.S. Cabinet, they might learn that the last thing the "capitalists" want is a war which will obliterate their investments at home and abroad.[3] Perhaps both parties might

---

[3] The first Eisenhower cabinet in 1953 was said to have been composed of "nine millionaires and a plumber."

begin to feel public opinion breathing down their necks! So far, although Foreign Offices do not stoop to this simple technique, many American business firms, some unions and lately the British Treasury are using it.

An American businessman, Ralph M. Besse of the Cleveland Electric Illuminating Company, has made another contribution to the study of behavior by stating some of the principles involved when an institutional change is contemplated. These principles apply, I believe, to nearly any institution, though they were designed for large corporations. A given change, says Mr. Besse, is more acceptable:

> When it is thoroughly understood in advance.
> When the people affected by it have helped to create its conditions.
> When it does not threaten their security.
> When it results from previously established principles rather than being dictated by fiat.
> When it is not introduced until after the last change has been well assimilated.[4]

WANTED: A DARWIN

Scientific studies in behavior are not a century old, and most of the careful work has been done in the last generation. The scientists are engaged, like Darwin and his contemporaries, in correcting, and sometimes overturning, the wisdom of the ages. The Darwinians corrected anti-knowledge about the age of the earth and the development of life. The behavioral scientists are correcting folklore about why we behave like human beings. Their path is far from smooth, but they meet no such fierce opposition as did the early evolutionists.

It is probable, furthermore, that a good deal of the wisdom of the ages concerning behavior will survive objective analysis. "Do as you would be done by" continues to be a sound operating principle.

---

[4] See also Lippitt and others, *The Dynamics of Planned Change* (Harcourt, Brace, 1958).

This chapter is a highly personal selection of certain aspects of behavioral science which constitute useful knowledge to me. Other generalists might make a different selection. I put the data to work every day, to help evaluate the headlines I read, the actions of people I encounter, the situations in meetings I attend, and especially to alleviate some of the fears and tensions in myself.

Any competent student of behavior will tell you that his knowledge is limited. Some segments here and there have been isolated and pinned down, but the laws for the whole grand design are few and far between. The area is dynamic, exciting, promising, but it has yet to find its Darwin.

16 . Economics for Generalists. I

LET US go back six thousand years and picture in our mind's eye the people in one of the temple cities of Sumeria. What are they doing there on the banks of the Euphrates on any given day? They are building houses, storing wheat and barley in the temple granary, inventing and fashioning new tools, weaving cloth, brewing beer, digging ditches, making love, rearing children, shearing sheep, designing pottery, praying to the gods, working in the fields around the city, trading with outsiders, keeping records, apportioning food, cooking, cleaning, quarreling, dancing, singing.

These activities, and many more which might be mentioned, are behavior patterns of the total culture, interwoven one with another and often impossible to separate, except verbally. A man may be composing a song while he plows a furrow, and a record keeper may think about expanding the alphabet to record more than temple inventories. The High Priest who leads in prayer to his official god is also the top manager of a complicated system whereby goods are produced and distributed.

Looking closer, we can pick out four sorts of activities primarily concerned with making a living, and so to be labeled *economic* behavior. A particular individual—the High Priest for example—may shift from an economic role to a religious role, to an artistic, educational or military role, as circumstances warrant. The economic roles include:

1. Producing things—food, houses, tools, clothes.
2. Distributing some of the things produced, especially food and clothing, to citizens.
3. Trading with outsiders—say bartering bronze axes for raw copper.
4. Bookkeeping.

Looking closer still, we see that these economic activities apply to goods for the long term and for the short term. Some of the production is solid and permanent, like the temple itself, the irrigation system, certain tools and equipment. Economists today call such output *capital goods*. The rest of the output is for more immediate consumption—food, fuel, pots, clothing, toys for the children—now called *consumer goods*.

The producers meanwhile consist of those who work primarily with their hands, and a much smaller group of managers, led by the High Priest, who direct the work after consulting the records and figuring out alternatives. So far as we know this division in Sumeria was based on merit, not on hereditary classes. The managers, we can assume, were near the high-IQ end of the frequency distribution curve.

THREE GREAT QUESTIONS

When we sum up this inspection, we realize that the patterns of economic behavior in Sumeria are also the main patterns operating in modern societies, with one conspicuous exception: the early cities had no money. They operated the economy on the basis of internal allocation and outside barter. The temple managers presumably decided what was to be produced, how much labor should go to capital goods and how much to consumer goods, how consumer goods were to be divided among citizens, what goods—such as copper or frankincense—were needed from sources outside the city, and what local products should be bartered for them.

Even without the invention of money, it does not take us
long to see in Ur the three great questions in economic behavior which have puzzled and plagued mankind ever since:

1. On what basis shall work be apportioned and food
allocated?

2. How much work must a citizen do to get his family
necessities? Implicit in this question are the modern problems
of hours, wages, prices, living standards, unions, labor-management relations.

3. On what basis shall total production be divided between
capital goods and consumer goods? In war, or the threat of
war, the question shifts to how much for arms and how much
for butter.

In Sumeria the temple management presumably made
these key decisions. In Russia today, the Presidium, after
consulting with various planning boards, presumably makes
them. In the United States today, authority is divided between the federal civilian government, the armed services,
the great corporations, the big unions, the farm lobby—all
pulling and hauling in various directions. Democracies
around the world similarly pull and haul.

Before Sumeria, nearly all work, whether of farmers,
herdsmen or hunters, went into consumer goods, primarily
food for today and a little for tomorrow. Civilization and the
production of capital goods came in together; they are indeed inseparable, for a city is work frozen in stone. Before
civilization the only capital goods were a few flints, possibly
a cleared field, possibly a crude storehouse for food. Caves
were made by nature, not by man. The Stone Age produced
almost no capital and achieved little in the way of economic
progress, but it had certain advantages. For instance, nobody
able to work was ever unemployed. All members of the band
shared what food there was, to the great benefit of morale.

A POTATO ECONOMY

The time came when the people of Mesopotamia invented
money to speed and standardize economic transactions—

perhaps the most important invention since that of grain. A generalist should know something about it beyond how to use money personally.

One way to grasp the function of money is to imagine a model community where people produce and consume nothing but one commodity, say potatoes. They appoint a manager, who gives out claim checks for a day's work in the fields. After the harvest is gathered, he finds that there are, let us say, four thousand bushels in storage and two thousand claim checks outstanding. Thus each check is good for two bushels, and the people line up, present their checks and carry away their share.

Here we have an economic model where money takes the form of claim checks and a perfect balance is maintained. The money flows out to workers, the goods flow in to storage; then the money flows to the warehouse, and potatoes flow out to the people. Finally the claim checks are torn up, and the cycle begins again.

What happens if claim checks are *not* torn up after harvest, and some people decide to save them? Then there will not be enough checks to redeem the total crop and some of the potatoes will spoil—or perhaps be dumped in the sea, like the coffee surplus of Brazil not many years ago. The system will not work long in a community where people hoard their claim checks; such a community had better abandon the invention and go back to barter.

If the saver invests in capital goods, however, the system can be made to work. The saver spends half his claim checks for potatoes, let us say, and gives the rest to a chap who has a plan for making a better type of plow. The latter collects his potatoes while working on the plow. All checks thus return to clear the crop. Next year, furthermore, production can be *increased* by using the better tool.

Our model thus outlines the production of consumer goods, the production of capital goods, and the distribution of consumer goods by means of claim checks based on work.

It does not show any gold, silver, wampum, cows, stone
wheels, or other things used for money over the ages.

"THE ROOT OF ALL EVIL"

The High Priest in the temple at Ur did not pass out claim
checks, but he gave orders for producing and distributing
goods which fulfilled much the same function, including the
allocation for better plows and other capital goods. Every
society must develop some method to solve these twin problems: the distribution of its potatoes and the manufacture of
its plows.

We do not know when money was first invented, but it is
logical to infer that barter, either with other temples or with
outside tribes, became increasingly clumsy as civilization
progressed. We can infer too that necessity was the mother
of this invention. We do know that gold coins were minted in
Lydia by King Croesus some twenty-five hundred years ago.

Until recent times, money has been a physical thing, valuable in its own right—furs, tobacco, cattle, slaves, mats,
cocoa, wampum, pieces of copper, iron, bronze, silver, and
above all gold. To complete any exchange, one swapped, say,
maize for wampum; then, at his convenience, he swapped
the wampum for a bow and arrow. When one bartered maize
for a bow and arrow the transaction was usually completed
at once; with wampum one could take his time and shop
around.

Observe that the monetary transaction is purely a man-
made convention, as much a part of the culture as the
proper behavior at a funeral—a bundle of rules, observances and taboos. Children must be taught how to behave
about money, much as they are taught how to behave at
table. They cannot take candy off the counter without sur-
rendering a piece of metal. It does not take them long to
learn that a green piece of paper is more valuable than a
green leaf.

After a society has adopted money in place of barter and
used it for a few generations, citizens come to regard it as

something fixed and eternal, with laws transcending human interference, like the solar system. It is at this point that specialists called economists, often armed with very formidable mathematics, seek to trace these supermundane laws. The generalist can be sure that none of these attempts has so far been successful. Why? Because the performance of money depends on how people *feel* at the time, and is thus primarily a function of behavior. The behavioral sciences have found a few scattered tendencies and trends which help our understanding, as well as some practical means of control, but the standard theories of both the classical *laissez faire* and the Marxian schools should not, in my opinion, be classed as useful knowledge. It is interesting to read about them, but they offer little to guide us in our problems today. Indeed, some of the propositions are dangerous anti-knowledge.

As the use of money spread, various taboos, compulsions and by-products developed. The nice equilibrium of the Stone Age band, or the Sumerian temple, or the potato model, was distorted. We note particularly how the use of money divided a society into those with a lot of it and those with little. Money tended to give power and prestige to the wealthy and thus a vested interest in keeping the poor poor.

INTEREST AND DEBT

The subsequent invention of a rate of interest on money promoted economic progress by making saving and capital formation more attractive. At the same time it promoted trouble by putting large numbers of people into debt, sometimes for life. Interest enabled certain citizens to live comfortably without working, on a logic of theoretic abstinence. In theory, that is, they had denied themselves earlier by tightening their belts, and now were receiving a just reward for their thrift and prudence. This logic has never been altogether convincing.

Various societies at various times have been forced to declare a moratorium, lest they founder in an ocean of debt.

The emperor Justinian enacted a general moratorium when
Italy was invaded by the Franks in 555 A.D. Some societies
have experimented with non-interest-bearing loans, and during World War II the United States invented an instrument
called "lend-lease," never seen before on land or sea, which
was partly gift, partly loan, and usually superior to considerations of interest. The Church in the Middle Ages banned
usury because of its many unfortunate effects on society.

BOOM AND BUST

The use of money in Western societies has led to an up-
and-down phenomenon known as the "business cycle." At
its extreme, this can bring a runaway inflation on the up side,
and mass unemployment on the down. In an inflation, claim
checks are dumped in the warehouse faster than the potatoes
come in, thus raising prices—i.e., the number of checks per
bushel. Or as we explain today, there is "more money than
goods." Sometimes, as in Germany in 1924, the spiral of inflation ascends so high that money becomes worthless, and a
new unit must be decreed by the government, wiping out
fixed incomes derived from bonds, pensions, annuities, as
well as debts. This painful process has occurred time and
again since money was first invented. The fear of it is behind
the demand that governments "balance the budget," and so
avoid flooding the economy with more money than goods.

A major depression is even more painful than a runaway
inflation, for it brings mass unemployment and often actual
hunger. As confidence wanes, the banks call loans and thus
dry up spending. There is usually no physical cause for a depression—no act of God, no drought, plague, earthquake.
All the productive equipment is in place, the prime movers
are ready to turn, and the unemployed eager to go to work.
The culture decrees, however, that goods must not move
without money to exchange for them, and until goods move,
the unemployed cannot work. So goods pile up on shelves,
the unemployed grow hungry, and society goes marching
grimly down the road to economic suicide. Finally some-

body in power may say the foolishness has gone far enough, and, to the consternation of the orthodox, proceed to lift a few of the taboos. What the temple priests of Ur would have made of a modern business depression is not difficult to imagine; they would have concluded that such a society was bereft of its wits—a surplus of food and hungry people; everything on hand ready to produce and no production! The curve of economic progress has gone downhill since Ur in this respect.

The lesson for generalists is not to blame any particular group but to blame the customs of the tribe, and to realize that money is a purely human construct, open to reasonable reconstruction if it fails to function. The phases of the moon we cannot change, the claim checks we can. In the next chapter I will offer a few suggestions.

MONEY AS PRESTIGE

Not only is a monetary system artificial, but it varies with the culture. A society where prestige depends on pecuniary values will have different rules for behavior from a society where it depends on aristocratic values, or military values, or religious values. Thus economic "laws" will vary with standards of behavior—a point not adequately considered by most economic theorists. Thorstein Veblen in *The Theory of the Leisure Class* made a brilliant beginning at considering it.

The United States has placed great store on pecuniary values, and this situation has caused a curious and often tragic myopia. Money being the most prized reward, other good things of life have been forced out of perspective. A beautiful building, or painting, or airplane, is often admired less for itself than for its gross cost. "Chicago's new $50,000,000 lake-front park" . . . "St. Thomas' proposed $20,000,000 cathedral" . . . "Rembrandt's prized $1,000,000 masterpiece." It takes a determined effort for the generalist, at least in America, to break through the curtain of dollars and see what lies behind, whether it be a fifty-million-dollar park, or a fifty-million-dollar string of highway signboards. Fortunately value systems change, and some observers already note a shift in the American culture away from the crass pecuniary standards of the Gilded Age.

THE RISE AND FALL OF GOLD

My grandfather, when I was a boy, used to give me a five-dollar gold piece on the Christmas tree. Later he made it a ten-dollar bank note, but the paper always seemed less satisfactory than the metal. I used to keep the gold piece and admire it for months; the bank note I soon spent. Gold was more than money then.

After experimenting with many varieties of commodity money, Western societies settled down some centuries ago to the use of gold as standard. It was heavy, beautiful, scarce, and hard to counterfeit. Gold pieces were passed from hand to hand in the purchase and sale of goods and services. The invasions of Mexico and Peru were motivated primarily by the lust for gold. The Aztecs, Maya and Incas had no such lust, and could not understand the passion of the invaders.

In due course most European countries substituted warehouse receipts for gold pieces. The receipts were easier to carry around, but metal to their full face value was held in the vaults of the bankers.

Then came a most significant change. Bankers found that as the gold was not often demanded, they could issue certificates, or promises to pay in gold, and so make profitable loans against *more* gold than they had in their vaults. Thus was modern money born—checkbook money, with nothing behind it except the hope of additional production to be financed by the loan. A large part of the money supply gradually became figures on a bank ledger, representing the banker's calculated risk that the loan would result in more goods.

In the United States today, money is represented by demand deposits in banks subject to written checks, and by currency issued by the government—paper dollars and stamped metal coins. The deposits are normally four to five times greater than the currency. There is a lot of gold in bars at Fort Knox in Kentucky, but nobody can use it without being jailed, and it is not counted as money in official statements.

MONEY AS NUMBERS

Modern money is created and extinguished by the banks in this fashion: You want, let us say, to build a motel on Highway 33. You take your plans to the bank and get a loan of $100,000. You receive no gold, of course, not even any currency, at least to begin with. The bank takes your note, puts it in the safe, along perhaps with your title deed as collateral, and opens a deposit account for you in its ledger. You are given a checkbook and told you can spend up to $100,000—less the bank's discount. Thus presto! the bank has put 100,000 new units in the national money system. When you pay off the loan, the 100,000 units vanish. In the depression of the 1930's, banks called loans right and left, causing billions of dollars to vanish. This reduced the power of people to spend, and made unemployment progressively worse.

A similar process of creating money occurs when governments, federal or local, sell bonds to the banks. The Treasury receives in effect a checkbook, and the bank receives government bonds for its portfolio. A new schoolhouse, a new dam, or a new anti-anti missile may result.

No matter how many numbers there are in the system, they do no good unless they are moving. Economists call their rate of motion the "velocity" of money. In a highly interdependent economy, the only final guarantee behind its money is the physical capacity to produce goods, and the human will to do so. Financial experts now declare that a society *can afford anything it can produce*. If the will to produce something is present—a behavioral motive, please observe—the money will be forthcoming, provided the banks have confidence (another psychological attribute) in the future of your motel, or whatever the proposition may be.

THE WILL TO PRODUCE

The destruction of the American fleet at Pearl Harbor in 1941 engendered in citizens a towering rage and a determined will to retaliate. The resulting activity not only ended the unemployment of the 1930's but created a labor shortage, and almost doubled annual production, including *both* guns and butter. New fleets were built, a vast new military establishment was created overnight, all without diminishing the annual output of consumer goods—though their distribution was largely shifted to the lower income groups. What many economists had said could not be done was done. Why? Because of that determined will.

After the war in 1945 most economists, including the author of this book, feared serious unemployment as war spending stopped. The American people, however, were in a mood to spend money for certain consumer goods which had gone out of production during the war, especially new houses and motorcars. The banks bowed to this desire, and created new money as described above. The war workers quickly found new jobs supplying the roaring demand. No better illustration could be given of the fact that behavior governs economics, or that modern money is highly elastic.

"The American people do not run around in sixty million automobiles because they are prosperous, no, they are prosperous *because* they run around in sixty million automobiles." This contemporary epigram contains a large element of truth. People want the cars and are willing to buy them on credit. The banks monetize the credit, dollars flow into the economy, and prosperity reigns. At least for a while.

The concept of metal as the only sound money, however, remains as a vigorous cultural lag in the minds of many estimable citizens. Gold, like barter, has proved too cumbersome and inelastic for practical use, especially in a time of rapid technological change. Gold began to go out of circulation as warehouse receipts came in many years ago, and now it is solemnly dug from a hole in the ground in South Africa and buried in another hole in the ground in Kentucky. Today, every country in the Western world manages its money through a central banking system, such as the Bank of England, or the Federal Reserve System in the United States.

Modern money meets modern needs far better than gold, but it does not maintain equilibrium as well as did the claim checks in the potato model. New monetary inventions are still badly needed. As the globe shrinks, and the sputniks circle around it in ninety minutes, a world economy will some day modify, if not displace, our national economies. We already have a World Bank, and before too long a world currency may become a mass demand.

17 . Economics for Generalists. II

THE ADVOCATES of gold—a declining but still vocal group—appear to believe that there is a fixed number of dollars, or pounds, or francs rattling around in the monetary system, and what one person gains another loses. It is therefore the duty of the prudent individual to see that the other fellow gains as little as possible. Most Americans do not now share this idea. They have grasped the high-wage, high-purchasing-power formula, first demonstrated by Henry Ford with the old Model T. Give the worker enough money, Ford said, to buy back the car he makes. A century ago, however, both in America and in Europe the fixed-fund idea was orthodox.

H. G. Wells in *The World of William Clissold* observes how businessmen of 1850 were convinced that economic progress depended on a large supply of cheap labor, and how they resisted trade unions and free public education. They underpaid their workers, who were further exploited by makers of shoddy and adulterated goods, by sub-landlords, and every sort of middleman. The old system, said Wells, "produced slums in every industrial center, and created swamps of agricultural laborers at the pauper level, slaves or peons, wherever it set up plantations. The creative industrialism of today, demanding a high type of labor and as much participation as possible, has no more use for slums and a reserve of unemployed than it has for ghettos and slave ships."

Economic times have changed, bringing a whole new philosophy of labor, wages and purchasing power, a philosophy which goes far to mitigate the class struggle as formulated by Karl Marx. Most people now believe that there must be enough claim checks distributed to redeem the potatoes, but a modern corollary warns that if claim checks are distributed more rapidly than potatoes are grown—that is, if purchasing power exceeds production—inflation will result. The high-wage economy always operates under this challenge.

COMMUNISM AND CAPITALISM

When he has acquired some useful knowledge about money, a generalist's view of economics is likely to turn to the great classic theories of *laissez faire* and Marxism. These historic doctrines were developed when factory workers put in an eighty-four hour week, and often lived in reeking slums on a miserable pittance. The passing of such conditions in the West has largely deprived the old doctrines of whatever relevancy they originally possessed. Yet a cultural lag in the form of slogans and clichés, by the "left" and by the "right," is embedded in the giant political struggle of our generation.[1] The slogans are often persuasive, and a generalist must keep his eye steadily on what workers, managers, bankers, and governments are actually doing, rather than what the time-honored doctrines and clichés say they are doing.

Moscow was broadcasting descriptions of the ragged factory workers and starving peasants of America at a time that the ragged workers were averaging eighty dollars a week, and many of the starving peasants, after getting the crop in, were driving their high-priced cars to Florida for the winter.

The American press meanwhile editorialized for years

---

[1] The study of economics used to be called "political economy," a more useful term, indicating the close connection between economic and political behavior.

about the impossibility of a Communist factory producing anything much beyond a wheelbarrow that would hold together. Russians, we were told, did not know a Stillson wrench from a crowbar, they lacked "know-how," and their system was deplorably weak on the proper incentives for production. Then the Russian-built satellites began circling the planet at eighteen thousand miles an hour in the fall of 1957, and the picture of Russia's technological ineptitude rapidly faded.

The prophets of capitalism were Adam Smith and David Ricardo, who argued that progress was best served by free competition among businessmen, with government regulation held to the minimum. The chief prophet of Communism was Karl Marx, who argued that progress was best served by the government running practically everything, with manual workers at the controls—the "dictatorship of the proletariat." Later the state would "wither away," he said. World peace, moreover, would automatically result from the world-wide unity of the working class.

Marx said that the rich would grow richer and the poor would grow poorer under capitalism—but the reverse has happened, aided by that great leveler, the graduated income tax. Smith and Ricardo said, in effect, that if everyone were free to pursue his private advantage, the economy would achieve an automatic equilibrium while producing more wealth. No society has ever dared to permit matters to go to such an extreme.

Looking beneath these competing ideologies, the objective student finds Americans, aided by private business, doing many things better than the Russians, while their life seems freer and pleasanter. He finds the Russians, aided by rigorous state controls, doing some things better than the Americans, such as training scientific specialists and building rockets.

GUNS OR BUTTER
In Sumeria, as we have seen, the High Priest decided how to apportion work between capital goods and consumer

goods. He had to figure how many man-hours could be spared from producing food to build, say, a new granary. Pharaoh had similar powers over a far larger realm, and so had most of the emperors, kings and potentates throughout recorded history. Indeed, to leave capital formation exclusively to private enterprise is taking a long chance, from the point of view of maximum survival for a given society. Suppose the enterprisers want to build a money-making race track when a non-money-making sewer system is badly needed? [2]

The Maya priests, the Incas, Alexander, Caesar, Louis XIV, Napoleon took no such chances. The Russians today are taking no such chances. This however is not necessarily "Communism" as advocated by Marx. It could equally well be an emulation of Peter the Great, who diverted enough labor to construct the splendid new city of St. Petersburg, and to introduce various capital improvements from the West. He had the power to give priority to guns or butter or palaces.

It took the United States a hundred years to create an industrial plant which has become the wonder of the world, using mainly the incentives of private enterprise, except in time of war. It has taken the Russians forty years to build a plant for heavy industry which is rapidly becoming productive and efficient. They had to overcome the terrible devastation wrought by Hitler's armies, and other handicaps; but they had modern technology to assist them.

It does not follow that Russians are smarter than Americans, only that capital formation is likely to accomplish more when it is directed to a specific goal. If a government has the power to keep citizens reasonably quiet on a low-calorie diet, while building steel plants, skyscrapers, submarines, sputniks and guided missiles, it stands to reason that capital

---

[2] Since I wrote these words, J. K. Galbraith has published a book, *The Affluent Society,* in which he holds that the United States is impoverished in many kinds of social wealth, through this same ill balance of capital investment.

goods, including armaments, can be accumulated at a high rate. Peter the Great may have accumulated them even faster than the present elite. Russian culture has been authoritarian for a thousand years, and most people were apparently willing to do the jobs ordered by Stalin as readily as the jobs once ordered by the czars.

It is dangerous to go so far off base as the American press, Congress and public opinion have recently gone in appraising the Russian economy. The European press has been more realistic. Generalists are likely to prefer the relative freedom of the American business system, but they cannot close their eyes to the fact that there are other ways of accumulating capital goods. China is following the Russian pattern at the moment, but it is essentially the same pattern as that which built the Great Wall during the Ming Dynasty. There is no particular reason to doubt that China will have an imposing industrial plant in another decade or two, if she can keep her people quiet on rice and water. Any docile society with access to modern technology can build an imposing plant.

GOVERNMENT AND BUSINESS

I recently attended a meeting of members of official zoning and planning boards, called to consider better ways and means to attract private industry to several neighboring towns. We spent a stimulating evening and produced a number of new ideas for enticing reluctant capitalists. That is, government men were trying to entice businessmen. Furthermore, many of our board members earn their living as businessmen. How does one unscramble this familiar situation in the Marxian–*laissez faire* dichotomy? As secretary of my town's planning board, was I a regimenting bureaucrat, or was I a supporter of private profiteering? Toss a coin for it.

Again, here is an article about the excellent work the American government has done controlling the Ohio River along its thousand-mile course from Pittsburgh to Cairo.[3] As a result, private industry in the Ohio Valley is booming as

[3] *The Reporter*, September 19, 1957.

never before. "How long will it be," the article concludes, "until there is an honest recognition that our economic system is a hybrid of public and private initiative, of public and private investment? There are many things that private enterprise can do better. But there are some things government can do better—among them the harnessing of rivers." One might add there are some things that co-operative societies, universities, foundations can do better than either government or businessmen.

Given the goal, what is the best agency to achieve it? Private business could not risk the losses which might come from trying to operate a complete national economic system, especially in the age of the atom. But sensible governments will utilize to capacity the special drive of private enterprise in the difficult years ahead. I was in Russia at the time when Lenin's New Economic Policy (NEP) was encouraging private business and foreign concessions, because of the collapse of the state marketing program. If Lenin had lived, perhaps he would have continued and expanded the NEP, to the great advantage of the Russian consumer.

People on the right who blanch at the word "socialism," as well as people on the left who blanch at the term "private enterprise," are rapidly becoming isolated from reality in a fog of slogans. No generalist will be terrified by either of these verbal spooks.

Take for instance the enormously important matter of the development of atomic power. It seems obvious that as in the case of the Ohio River, government must take the lead, contracting basic research from the universities, and encouraging private business to shoulder much of the responsibility for future technical operation. In such a practical program the "rights" and "lefts" are impotent, their chief contribution a series of stale clichés and competing catcalls.

THE MANAGERIAL REVOLUTION

Let us look at some economic changes in capitalistic societies undreamed of by Marx and Ricardo. Among the more significant are the "welfare state," the rise of the service trades, the rise of labor unions with their "fringe benefits," techniques for controlling the business cycle, and perhaps most important of all, the so-called managerial revolution.

Both Marx and Ricardo identified "capitalist" with "property owner," and assumed further that every business was run by its owners. Today in America, and to a lesser degree in Europe, the stockholders of most large corporations, though the legal owners, have lost control of the business. They have been displaced by self-perpetuating managements which may own no stock at all, or only a minority. At the time of the classic study of this profound shift, made by A. A. Berle, Jr., and Gardiner Means, only 12 per cent of the two hundred largest nonbanking corporations in the United States remained under the control of their legal owners.[4] There is no reason to suppose that the trend has been reversed, but rather the contrary. Stockholders, who exert less and less power, rarely complain, provided they receive their conventional dividends.

The managerial revolution is a natural outgrowth of increasing specialization and size. A million stockholders are not competent to make decisions for a billion-dollar corporation. Specialists in management not only operate big corporations, but are found in government departments and in many large nonprofit institutions. It is said that the huge Russian trusts, producing coal, steel, oil, and the rest, have evolved a type of manager not too dissimilar from those found in corner offices in Pittsburgh, Chicago and New York. Why not? The technical tasks of managing men, materials and machines are very similar. It is chiefly in the sales department that activities will differ. Russian trusts are expected to show a financial profit, but there is little competi-

---

[4] *The Modern Corporation and Private Property* (Macmillan, 1933). Mr. Berle brings the figures up to date in *Economic Power and the Free Society*, a pamphlet published by The Fund for the Republic, 1957.

tion in the American sense, and output is allocated according to plans made higher up. How much steel shall go to tanks, and how much to pleasure cars is not for the manager of the steel trust to say.

Meanwhile in Russia prices are administered, or set, by the government; in America by the big corporations, in many cases.

THE WELFARE STATE

The managerial revolution in the West has developed along with powerful unions, and a great increase in governmental functions. In the United States the federal government is taking in taxes about half the annual profits, to become in effect the silent partner in every profitable corporation. It is taking up to 90 per cent of the income of wealthy individuals. Both British and American governments—the ardent protectors of capitalism, according to Moscow—operate a gigantic equalizer, which scoops dollars and pounds from the top of the economy and shovels them in by the billions at the bottom. The money from the top goes for old-age pensions, social-security payments, subsidies to farmers, relief of the indigent, and other disbursements of the welfare state; Britain adds a complete health service for every family.

American unions meanwhile are now powerful enough to bargain collectively with the great corporations for the highest real wages the world has ever seen. Even without unions in some occupations, however, wage rates would have risen substantially during the past thirty years. Ford had no unions in his plant when he inaugurated the high-wage philosophy. British unions not only possess great power in collective bargaining, but are the backbone of the British Labour Party, which runs the country from time to time.

THE SERVICE TRADES

Another huge economic change not anticipated in classical theory is the massive shift to the "tertiary" or service trades in modern industrialized societies. When the industrial revolution was gathering headway, at the time of the American political revolution, the ratio of farmers to the gainfully employed in the United States was 90 per cent or more. As machines and factories came in, that ratio fell, while the proportion of industrial workers rose. But about the year 1920 in America, the ratio of industrial workers halted its hundred-year rise, fell a little, while the agricultural ratio fell still further. The service trades shouldered out both. Today more than half the gainfully employed are not in the fields (the sickle), nor in the factory (the hammer), but are clerks, shopkeepers, professional people, teachers, government employees, TV service men, disc jockeys, ball players, truck drivers, and the hordes who line the highways furnishing food, lodging, gasoline and entertainment.

Meanwhile, automation and agricultural research are steadily increasing output per man-hour on the farm and in the factory—a change as revolutionary in its way as the high-wage doctrine of Henry Ford, and an integral part of it. The smaller the proportion of primary workers needed, the more the service trades expand—happily so, or mass unemployment would result. Out of the rise in production per man-hour, the higher wages are paid, and the work week is reduced.

THE BUSINESS CYCLE

A closed economy like that of Russia does not suffer from a business cycle. Central planning can prevent overproduction, or correct it quickly if it begins to develop. For years to come, moreover, the Russians are likely to suffer from underproduction.

In the West, the depression of the 1930's may have been the last catastrophic collapse. Why? Because we know a number of effective methods for stopping a downswing, and a popular government which fails to apply this knowledge will soon be out of office. Politicians are notoriously averse to being out of office.

The principal controls to apply are three:

First, an easing of credit, so that people may borrow and spend more readily as the banks create more money.

Second, a reduction in taxes, primarily income taxes, so that people are encouraged to spend more freely for consumer goods.

Third, an increase in government spending, primarily for public works. Every government needs a stockpile of such plans, carrying a maximum of employment, for rapid expansion when a recession is indicated.

These remedies are now widely accepted even by conservatives, though they may create a budget deficit. Income-tax reduction was used with good effect in the United States in halting the recessions of 1949 and 1954. Also we now have built-in brakes, absent in the great depression of the thirties: unemployment insurance, social security payments, subsidies to farmers, and especially the government guarantee of individual bank deposits up to $10,000, which should largely prevent the runs on banks that proved so disastrous in earlier depressions.

World War II taught many useful financial lessons, with the help of a brilliant economist, John Maynard Keynes. He worked out the method which successfully stopped inflation, something hitherto unheard of in wartime. Similar methods could stop it in peacetime, if democratic governments were able to enforce or induce a Spartan thrift and renunciation. Here the controls are the *opposite* of those for recession, namely, higher interest rates to discourage borrowing, higher taxes, a reduction of government outlay, and a big budget surplus.

J. K. Galbraith in *The Affluent Society* makes the point that the insistence on full employment today is forcing a high level of production to provide jobs—any old kind of production. This requires in turn ever more fantastic salesmanship, and ever more consumer credit to move the goods, accompanied by ever more inflation. He terms it an economic squirrel cage, which will not indefinitely revolve. "To create the demand for new automobiles," he says, "we must contrive elaborate and functionless changes each year [planned obsolescence] and then subject the consumer to ruthless psychological pressures to persuade him of their importance. Were this process to falter or break down, the consequences would be disturbing." Detroit is seriously disturbed as I write, with nearly a million new cars unsold.

Beyond the business cycle, which may operate in only one society, looms the world economy that the shuttle of technology is inexorably weaving. Already any recession in the United States can soon affect the whole so-called "free world." It will affect the whole planet if and when trade routes multiply through the Iron and Bamboo curtains. What world-wide controls can be devised to keep unemployment—or inflation—from developing then? It is none too soon for specialists to begin working on them.

FRINGE BENEFITS

Another change to make classicists turn in their graves is the result primarily of collective bargaining between union and employer. Managers in America, and to a lesser extent elsewhere in the West, are experimenting with a number of devices called "fringe benefits" for employees—pension funds, insurance, profit-sharing plans, longer vacations, the five-day week, courses of study both general and technical. Social scientists retained by management also conduct research into the way executives make decisions; into the attitudes of employees toward the job, the boss and the company; into the structure of informal groups in the shop; two-way communication systems between men and management; and the relations of the company with the outside community.

If the American schoolroom is filled with "frills" today, they are nothing compared to the frills in the up-and-coming giant corporation, that monster which is supposed to be devoted to grinding the faces of the poor. The fact that these experiments can be charged off as a legitimate cost in the income-tax return is no small encouragement. At the same time it has been well established that satisfied employees are more productive, and a shop full of good human relations is preferable to a shop full of bad ones. This extensive work in labor-management relations is part and parcel of the behavior studies cited in Chapter 15.

REALITY VERSUS IDEOLOGY

It is curious, indeed tragic, how tangible behavior belies the economic ideology of both East and West. So far as we know, there has never been a serious strike in Russian industry. This is not because the workers are so contented, but because if they walk out they are extremely likely to be shot. As long ago as the late 1920's, the trade unions were in the process of being stripped of independent action, to become a part of the apparatus of the state. I talked to many of their leaders at the time. The condition of workers in the West is far happier and freer, with their strong independent unions, their high wages, short hours, fringe benefits, and the right to walk out if they do not like the job.

In brief, many of the evils charged by Russians against the West the Russians themselves nourish. Yet in certain fields Russians have equaled or surpassed the over-all efficiency upon which the West prides itself, chiefly by allocating production to specific goals.

It would be a better-adjusted world if Russian workers had the benefits enjoyed by the employees, say, of the Standard Oil Company of New Jersey, and if Western societies could steer more of their output into essential enterprises like schoolhouses, and less into foolish and wasteful ones like fin-tail cars and billboards.

The new nations springing up around the world today have a difficult road ahead of them in many respects, not the least in planning their economic future. Utopia is not

to be won by either of the classic formulas. If they go
Communist, and can keep their people on Spartan rations,
they can build up heavy industry quite rapidly. If they go
all out for free enterprise, their people will be happier and
better fed—until a depression or a squirrel cage inflation
comes along.

SUMMARY

This chapter and the preceding one deal with matters
commonly called "economic." Although something of a
specialist in this department, I have tried to treat it in a
way which can readily be followed and provides useful
knowledge for generalists in evaluating economic problems
today. Not yesterday—today. Three major points have been
made which will bear repeating:

1. Economics is largely a function of behavior in a given
culture, and can claim few independent "laws." Different
cultures generate different economic behavior—as in the
varying attitudes toward money. All attempts to establish
over-all, full-whiskered economic theory have failed. Lesser
propositions, such as the managerial revolution, the growth
of the service trades, methods for controlling the business
cycle, are more helpful. Economic statistics, aided by electronic computers, are increasingly helpful, and promise to
lay the groundwork for better theory.[5] (Professor Schum-
peter of Harvard once said, as he contemplated the flood
of modern statistics: "How nice economics was before anybody knew anything!")

2. Money is a man-made complex of habit and custom,
garnished with pieces of metal and paper. Lately it has
become very flexible, in the form of numbers appearing
and vanishing on the ledgers of banks. It has no immutable
laws; theoretically monetary customs could be changed at

---

[5] Such as Leontiev's Input-Output Analysis, where the output of one industry becomes the input of another, and the whole economy is compre-
hended in one tremendous balance sheet.

our convenience. Serious inflations and depressions are in one sense a form of cultural lag.

3. The conflict between "capitalism" and "Communism," publicized extravagantly in both Moscow and Washington, bears little relation to economic operations actually in progress around the world. Nobody knows, for instance, where the great corporation is going—not even its managers. We can be reasonably sure, however, that it is not going to run either the country or the planet.

The Big Brain has not particularly distinguished itself on the economic front since Sumeria. Our technological progress has been stupendous, but we have not yet learned, in either the West or the East, to fit the pieces together in a secure and livable scheme.

18 . Political Behavior

COMPETITION for leadership is found in every human society, whatever its political structure. Somebody must direct the various activities, from a square dance to the production of steel, and somebody must lead the band as a whole. Politics is concerned with seizing or attaining power: "Who's in charge around here?" Political behavior is in evidence, both inside the band and between competing bands.

The serious conflict now raging between the American and Russian bands, which in the preceding chapter we looked at as a competition between rival ideologies, can also be viewed as a straight power struggle. Though they have twice been comrades in arms, today they are contending in a crisis of power politics, complicated by the unprecedented factor of atomic weapons.

War has ever been the last resort of competing sovereign states, and usually has brought more power to the winner. But now nobody can "win" an all-out war. Testimony of nuclear physicists makes it clear that the two great powers will only destroy themselves with resounding finality, leaving political power, if any, in the hands of Eskimos and Solomon Islanders. Only a madman can push the button— which is not to say that Hitler was the last of the madmen. General Omar Bradley puts it this way: "We reason that no government, not even one willful individual, would be so foolhardy, so reckless, as to precipitate a war which will most surely end in mutual destruction. . . . But even logic sometimes goes awry."

Statesmen and politicians do not know how to act in their new roles, so they continue to bluster and make dire threats as of old, but their appeals to the flag and the sword are becoming less effective. For the first time, leaders fear their own power. A terrible choice faces them: either to blow up the world or to sacrifice sovereignty and possibly surrender their country without a fight. If politics, in the classic phrase, is "the art of the possible," then its dimensions have drastically altered since Hiroshima. The possible has grown to include mutual annihilation, and also, if nuclear weapons are diffused, awesome power will accrue to small states hitherto disregarded.

In this predicament, what is the proper behavior for heads of state who dare no longer mount, or even seriously threaten, a general war? Nobody knows. Presidents, prime ministers, generalissimos are floundering in a sort of political vacuum. Their dilemma, and the dilemma of this age, is admirably summarized by an old Indian on a reservation in Idaho:

> You white people seem to be a very funny people, who are always talking about your atom bombs you are going to kill people with. Now that you have managed to get most of you settled down in a dozen or more of the larger cities, I suppose some day some crazy fool will begin to throw atom bombs around. If he does, it will kill enough of you white people so that the few who are left, won't be too many left, and we will fight and beat the daylights out of you, and we will take our country back.[1]

THE PEOPLE YES AND NO

As in the case of economics, politics is a function of behavior, and shifts with the culture. Very few comprehensive

---

[1] Quoted in a letter to the author from a friend in Idaho.

"laws" have yet been established. Various principles of behavior discussed in earlier chapters might be termed "political"—such as the concept of mass wants. Political scientists, moreover, like economists increasingly wary of over-all theory, are turning to a study of ways and means for meeting specific political situations. They are conducting research into the behavior of people in legislative, executive and judicial posts. They are analyzing voting behavior by advanced techniques in opinion polling, and sounding out mass opinion on political questions. The dynamic data gained in these studies are replacing the old organization charts, which showed the formal structures of government according to the formal constitution.

Power gives its owner prestige, a high place in the pecking order, income and security—at least for a time. Many industrial leaders have these attributes of power, but only government leaders may use the police and the army to enforce their commands. "Political power carries with it the supreme sanction of life or death," says Peter Odegard.

Rulers normally rationalize their use of force by appealing to popular symbols and slogans—the Voice of the People, Natural Law, the Security of the State, and until recent times, the Divine Right of Kings. Political scientists are increasingly shy of moral judgments, content to describe political behavior and try to account for its motivation. Odegard notes too that American courts are beginning to base decisions on data from the behavioral sciences, as well as on legal precedents.

WIND RIVER PEOPLE

Stone Age bands seem to have been loose, freewheeling small democracies. They almost certainly had a leader, but not the Old Man with club and prostrate female. Unfortunately it is impossible to observe a band of hunters in transit along the Danube ten thousand years ago, but we have careful descriptions by anthropologists of Indian bands in North America, who followed a similar way of life.

Here, for instance, are the Shoshone Indians of the Wind River country in Wyoming and Idaho.[2] Before they were overrun by white settlers, less than a hundred years ago, they lived in kinship bands of forty to fifty persons under a petty chief. The band looked to this chief for such decisions as when to move, where to look for food, at what season to leave the prairie for the hills. If people found his decisions unwise they selected a new leader.

The Shoshones broke wild horses and held a big annual buffalo hunt, participated in by a number of bands. A chief would be chosen to lead this year's joint hunt, next year another chief. When the Shoshones went to war with the Blackfeet or the Crows, a special war chief was elected; if still alive at the end of the war his task was over. Other leaders were chosen for special dances and ceremonies. The only Shoshone tribe which had hereditary chiefs was a settled people along the river, where the fishing was good. When a band lived in one place for years, it developed a more complex administration and preferred a permanent leader. One might cautiously generalize from this account of the Wind River Indians that roving bands tended to be politically very democratic, and settled bands less so— the forerunners of settled city folk.

THE DEMOCRATIC MODEL

Ur, as we have seen, was a theocracy with temple priests in charge, but apparently a beneficent one, as were the priest-ruled cities of the Maya. Many experiments have since been made in political structure, and a number of models are still on display, including some by nature peoples as well as by civilized tribes.

Two general types predominate today: political democracy, as in Britain, Sweden and the United States; autocracy as in Russia, China and Saudi Arabia. A democracy requires a large, literate middle class for successful operation. Many Latin American states have excellent constitutions guaran-

2 Unpublished paper by Mary Lou Skinner, August, 1957.

teeing democracy, but in the absence of a powerful middle class, power tends to drift from one strong man to another. The basic rights of a democracy are these:

> The right of citizens to join political parties, and to elect and dismiss leaders at legal intervals.
> Freedom of speech, press and religion.
> The right of equal protection under the law.
> No citizen to be deprived of life, liberty or property except by due process of law: trial by jury, protection against search and seizure, and against self-incrimination (the famous Fifth Amendment to the U.S. Constitution), and the assumption by the courts of innocence until guilt is proved.

These rights are not always lived up to, but they are approached. Countries with a homogeneous population, like Britain and Sweden, live up to them rather better than the United States—which has the special problems of a large Negro population, and another large percentage from alien cultures, welcomed by the liberal immigration laws of years ago. The era of "McCarthyism" in the early 1950's showed how far the United States could depart from its formal political structure, as well as democratic behavior, under the pressure of fear and uncertainty about America's new role in the world.

Production, distribution and new investment in the democracies are largely in the hands of businessmen, except in time of war.

THE AUTOCRATIC MODEL

In Russia, China and other autocracies—not all subscribing to Communism by any means—a very different pattern is in evidence. Often it looks like this:

> A single political party, with opposition leaders likely to be shot or exiled.
> A terroristic police apparatus. The accused is assumed guilty until he can prove his innocence.
> A monopoly of mass communication—press, radio, telephone, telegraph, television—together with strict censorship.

A frozen frontier, called by Churchill an iron curtain.

Rigid state control of money, banking and foreign exchange.

The arbitrary allocation of labor and materials to capital goods, usually at the cost of consumer goods, as explained in preceding chapters.

Sometimes an elaborate ideology, such as Marxism or Fascism, complete with prophets, ikons and sacred books, *Das Kapital, Mein Kampf*. Students have compared these ideologies to a religion.

Generalists interested in acquiring useful knowledge may find the monopoly and manipulation of the mass media perhaps the most abhorrent item on the above list. It is terrible to us to think of 200 million Russians, many of them very intelligent and observing, cut off for forty years from objective knowledge of the world both inside and outside their country, and even worse, fed a diet of anti-knowledge about the rest of the world. We must remember, however, that the Russian emphasis on educating scientists, screening every talented child, is bound to develop an educated middle class. Not only are the youngsters rigorously disciplined in science, but many do not take their political indoctrination very seriously. The scientific attitude is eternally at war with dogma. How long will the dam of anti-knowledge hold in Russia?

Americans, too, have been indoctrinated with many half-truths and plain lies about Russia. But no policeman can stop an American from consulting responsible sources of information, such as the Russian research centers at Harvard and Columbia and books and documents in public libraries. The facts about Russia are there if one cares to go and get them. It is not unfair, I think, to speak of the democracies as relatively *open* societies, and the autocratic models as *closed* societies. A number of nations now included in the "free world" are closed societies, the Dominican Republic, for instance.

A GOVERNMENT THAT CAN GOVERN

Much as one may prefer the democratic model to the autocratic, he can hardly acclaim any existing democracy as perfect. The American model suffers from inflexibility, in that power can legally change only once in four years. The French model suffers from being too flexible, with a cabinet crisis every few months, until a de Gaulle has to be summoned to take over.

Most American state legislatures do not represent the present population distribution between city men and country men. A cultural lag, called the "rotten borough" system, gives the farmer an unfair control of the legislature. My rural town of 3,500 elects two members to the Connecticut lower house, no fewer than the city of Bridgeport elects, with a population of 160,000.

The two-party system was not favored by the American founding fathers (who were all generalists, by the way), but it works a good deal better than the multiparty system of France. Its major drawbacks are the unending creation of *political* rather than honest disagreement on important issues, and a party loyalty which often transcends common sense. A state boss once said in my hearing, "If the Devil were heading the Republican ticket, and Jesus Christ was the Democratic candidate, I'd vote for the Devil every time!" It is increasingly difficult for a generalist to be a passionate party man in the United States—and probably in most other countries as well. He can be passionate about a given political issue, but he leaves undeviating adherence to party to the politically immature. Knowing what he knows about the biology of racial differences, he can no more be a loyal Democrat on all issues in America than he can be a loyal Labour Party man in Britain, knowing what he knows about the trend of economics and the folly of nationalizing everything.

In one sense, it is here in the field of politics that the generalist comes into his own. A civilian voter *must* be a kind of generalist, for if he were a true specialist in politics he would have to be a professional administrator or office seeker. On the wisdom, fairness, information and responsibility of voters with this approach, the success of political democracy depends.

What kind of government should a generalist support? I suspect he will favor "a government which can govern," which has a policy and the power and determination to carry it out. But he will insist that it be legally subject to removal when its policies conflict too long and too sharply with popular wants and needs. He would welcome an expert civil service like that of Britain, insulated from changes in party and aided by various new administrative techniques and tools, such as electronic computers. He would welcome gratefully a political leadership which heeded the famous plea of Adlai Stevenson to "talk sense."

The generalist follows with interest the scientific sampling of public opinion by accredited polling organizations, as it improves in accuracy, and focuses more sharply on suitable problems. He might like to see a trial of Elmo Roper's idea whereby a Bureau of Opinion Research, as impartial and objective as the Supreme Court, would continually poll public opinion on important current questions, in the effort to keep the government aware of what people are wanting and thinking, and aware of areas of public ignorance. The generalist realizes of course that the voice of the people is not the voice of God, and that a wise leadership may have to run counter to popular opinion in some matters in order to meet fundamental needs in others. It goes without saying that such a bureau would never have anything to do with election polling.

It would be pleasant too if citizens could come to regard an election as less like a horse race and more like an important personal decision, such as buying a new house. As matters now stand, the technical arrangements of the mass media for reporting the Kentucky Derby, the World Series in baseball, and the nomination and election of the President of the United States, are remarkably similar. "Who's going to win? What are the betting odds?"

The reconciliation of popular government with mature judgment is surely one of the great questions for the political future. The fact that the generalist prefers democracy to autocracy does not make it any easier for him to listen to most political speeches. When popular education improves, however, and more citizens begin to use their minds at somewhere near biological capacity, solutions which now seem impossible may not prove too difficult. They will turn, I suspect, on the technical problem of maintaining enough tension through parties or otherwise to force competent performance by the government in power, without creating those bogus political conflicts which are the despair of reasonable men.

NATIONALISM AS A CULTURAL LAG

The sovereign state as we know it today, with its accredited symbols of flag, anthem, military and diplomatic establishments, frontier guards, passports, currency and customs houses, is a relatively recent invention, dating from the Peace of Westphalia in the seventeenth century—and of no particular credit to the inventors, if I may say so.

Most men have always preferred their own mountains or coasts, their own language and people—not only preferred but loved them with a deep nostalgic feeling that at times can surpass or encompass the primary emotional drives. "So and no otherwise, hillmen desire their hills." When these deep feelings become geared to the mechanics of military nationalism, the results are usually explosive, if not disastrous.

Any modern state is a society organized primarily for battle. The budget of practically every one of them shows a commanding percentage devoted to war.[3] The military

---

[3] The U.S. federal budget for the fiscal year ended June 30, 1959, gives a "combined total of all spending related to war of $61.6 billion, or 83 per-

and diplomatic apparatus is normally set up to defend to the death every foot of native soil, and hopefully to seize any other parcels of real estate not belligerently defended. Regard the behavior today of a dozen sovereign states shaking with real-estate trouble. Regard in your imagination the reaction of the American people if it were proposed that Mexico should re-annex a few square miles of her ancient holdings in Texas.

This real-estate complex of nations is of course cultural, and by no means universal. American Indians regarded land as a game preserve, and often thought they were selling hunting rights to white settlers, rather than a fee simple. Stone Age bands roamed where they willed over the continents. The vast Church lands of the Middle Ages were uncomplicated by nationalism.

> Legally the world's affairs are in the control of a miscellany of sovereign states, and each embodies itself in a government of politicians and officials, deeply concerned in maintaining the bargaining autonomy of the particular regime which gives them importance, and prepared to offer a spirited resistance to any invasion, conquest or amalgamation. . . .[4]

Today some fifty societies, once colonies or dependencies of the Atlantic powers, are freshly drawn upon the map as fullfledged nations, with political leaders eager for the power, prestige and perquisites appropriate to a sovereign state. The populace is to be taxed, or the United States Treasury is to be tapped, or both, for a full complement of tanks, war planes, submarines, uniforms, medals, ambassadorial suites at the Waldorf, local currency, postage stamps, and customs officials. These trappings and lethal hardware appear ironically at the moment when most armaments are becoming as obsolete as a Bronze Age battle-ax, and when

---

cent of the entire budget. Our peace budget, in other words, would be a mere $12.3 billion."—Editorial in *New York Times*, January 16, 1958. A major reason for the current prosperity of West Germany is that it is prevented by treaty from spending great sums for weaponry.

4 H. G. Wells: *The Fate of Man* (Longmans, Green, 1939).

every penny of taxation or foreign aid is needed to equip the
new nation with roads, schools, hospitals, power plants, irrigation canals, conservation projects and other peacetime
capital outlays.

All this, though it is both foolish and tragic, is quite understandable. The new nations have been submerged for many
years, some of them for centuries, as items in the white man's
burden. Now they want to prove to the world that they are
as good as anybody else, which involves parading in the
standard paraphernalia.

There is a further complication: while dominated by outsiders, a society can hardly develop local leaders. When
the domination is removed, it finds itself with a shortage of
trained administrators. The new governments are thus likely
to be shaky until a tradition of leadership is established. In
Puerto Rico the situation was met by Governor Rexford
Tugwell in the early 1940's and by Luis Muñoz Marín, now
governor, who, working together, developed a cadre of brilliant young administrators by first sending them to universities and technical schools on the mainland.

When a neighboring state is behaving in an irritating way,
the generalist might remember the adage that "forty million
Frenchmen can't be wrong." The people there follow the
frequency distribution curve, like the people of his own native land—with saints and sinners at either end. Leaders
may be behaving badly, the rank and file may be seriously
misinformed, but a prime test of a generalist is that he never
damns a society as a whole.

WORLD MEN AND THE WORLD COMMUNITY

On balance it is certainly a gain to have the new nations
out from under the yoke of colonialism. One wonders however how they can function as sovereign states, touchy about
rights and real estate, and at the same time be serviceable
members of that world community which the age demands.
Their leaders cannot play lead soldiers indefinitely. Their
budgets cannot long tolerate the dead waste of a large
military establishment. This holds for the Great Powers

too, but is more acute among the new members of the United Nations. A formula is badly needed which can combine local pride and autonomy with planetary co-operation, and it must apply to all the nations of the world, great and small.

International co-operation meanwhile goes on smoothly in many nonpolitical fields. Among the scores of international agencies and systems set up to fill a specific need, we find:

The Postal Union
The Red Cross
The metric system
Greenwich Time
International weather reports
International airports and air controls
International Geographical Union—now mapping the land of the world
International Geophysical Year
International Seismological Summary, which works on earthquakes from data sent by world-wide stations
Nobel Prizes
Olympic Games
Scientific, cultural and religious international conferences.
And of course
Miss Universe.

Meanwhile France, Germany, Italy, Belgium, the Netherlands and Luxembourg are inaugurating a kind of United States of Europe, with supranational controls over coal, steel, atomic energy, and looking toward a free-trade area of seventeen European nations including Britain, with a total population of 250 million.

People who scoff at any attempted organization of the world community should look at the record. Not only have international agencies increased since the formation of the United Nations, but, as Raymond B. Fosdick eloquently points out, they have been operating for a long time.[5]

---

5 *Within Our Power, Perspective for a Time of Peril* (Longmans, Green, 1952).

For the first time in history, a basis has been laid for a unified world. . . . Slowly and almost without our knowing it, the intellectual life of the world has been largely internationalized. . . . In World War II, an American soldier wounded on a battlefield in the Far East owed his life to the Japanese scientist, Kitasato, who isolated the bacillus of tetanus. A Russian soldier saved by a blood transfusion was indebted to Landsteiner, an Austrian. A German soldier was shielded from typhoid with the help of a Russian, Metchnikoff. A Dutch marine in the East Indies was protected from malaria because of the experiments of an Italian, Grassi; while a British aviator in North America escaped death from surgical infection because a Frenchman, Pasteur, and a German, Koch, elaborated a new technique.

The virus strain on which a successful yellow-fever vaccine was developed, Mr. Fosdick continues, was taken from a Negro named Asibi in West Africa, sick with yellow fever. The specimen was inoculated into a rhesus monkey. Asibi recovered but the monkey died. All the vaccine since manufactured goes back to Asibi: "the blood of one man in Africa has been made to serve the whole human race."

THE UNITED NATIONS

The United Nations is now our outstanding agency of internationalism, but it must be strengthened if it is not to go down like the League of Nations. If it does go down, the world will promptly demand another one, but with years of momentum lost. Among the improvements which have been suggested and seem appropriate as I write are these:

The abolition of the veto.

Some system of weighted voting for certain types of questions, so that Ghana or Honduras does not balance off the Soviet Union or the United States.

A permanent international police force, controlling all nuclear weapons.

The power to accept and administer mandated territory—

say Antarctica, where a dreadful row over real estate is in the making.[6]

A determined attempt to legislate the control of space, which up to now is free from vested interests—unless you count those of Jules Verne and H. G. Wells. The United Nations has no time to lose, for once outer space gets into the real-estate syndrome of the U.S. or Russia, this unprecedented opportunity to advance internationalism will be lost.

The promotion of world communication and a world language. (The latter commented on in Chapter 14.)

The development of tough arbitration machinery, probably in conjunction with the World Court. Conflict between states will hopefully be settled here, rather than on the atomic battlefield.

The promotion of a world currency, and a steady push toward world free trade.

An over-all plan for husbanding the world's natural resources, balancing them against the curve of population.

It will take administrator-philosophers to carry forward such programs; men and women who devote their lives to serving not "Ruritania," but all mankind. Every one of them will have to be a generalist.

---

6 By 1958, territorial claims were in the wind for Britain, France, Argentina, Chile, Australia, New Zealand, the United States and Russia.

19 . The Scientific Attitude

THE SCIENTIFIC ATTITUDE has been at work ever since man was man—probably long before he developed any formal system of religion. It produced the first flint tools, the first bow and arrow, the first tame goat, the first field of maize, the first wheel. Rather than relying on intuition, or the ways of the fathers, or the configuration of the stars, a man takes a stone and a chunk of flint and begins to chip—first this way, then that: "No, that doesn't work; ah, now it's taking shape, this is how to do it!"

The man is following trial and error, a preliminary stage in the development of science. Up to the time of the Greeks this was the only method; it built the temples of Ur, the pyramids of Egypt and Mexico, the hanging gardens of Babylon. One of the strangest things it produced was the boomerang of Australia. The siphon was employed, but nobody knew *why* water would run uphill in a pipe, for the laws governing air pressure had of course not been worked out. The Greeks discovered some of the whys, but as their laboratory facilities were severely limited, they could not do much to check their theories. It remained for Galileo, Newton, Einstein and the age of modern science to develop the grand principles governing the why of things and the behavior of certain aspects of the universe.

The first and second laws of thermodynamics are excellent examples of science finding the answer to the why of things. After their formulation, some two centuries ago, attempts to invent perpetual motion machines were abandoned, by all except crackpots. The performance of heat engines is governed by thermodynamics, and the laws help to explain transformations of energy everywhere.

Most of the useful knowledge so far set forth in this book has come from the work of high specialists in science, a little from lay observers informed with the scientific attitude. Animals can sometimes solve a problem by trial and error, like a cat in a maze. Only human beings, however, helped by languages, can explain what has been done and record it for others to verify and build upon—making a more accurate bow and arrow, a sturdier strain of corn. Technology builds like a team of acrobats standing on one another's shoulders —if one could imagine a team that has grown over the centuries to include a host of performers. The man on the bottom was the Stone Age hunter with his problem of flaking flint.

Said Lord Ernest Rutherford, the great physicist, in concluding a lecture on atomic structure:

> Science goes step by step, and every man depends on the work of his predecessors. When you hear of a sudden unexpected discovery . . . you can always be sure that it has grown up by the influence of one man on another, and it is this mutual influence which makes the enormous possibility of scientific advance . . . the combined wisdom of thousands of men, all thinking the same problem, and each doing his little bit to add to the great structure of knowledge which is gradually being erected.

WHAT SCIENCE DOES TO US

Thus the increase proceeds at an exponential rate, irreversibly, each discovery leading to new discoveries, and all affecting people everywhere in many unsuspected ways. The world is today in the grip of applied science, but few of us realize how tightly it holds us all. With the tenacity of an ice age it limits our personal lives from day to day, as well as all national and global activities; when the electric current goes off, we suddenly realize our utter dependence.

Take one gross effect of medical science. The sudden, explosive increase in population the world around is the direct result of scientific progress—not greater fertility, but a drastic reduction in the death rate, due to modern medicine. The great plagues which once scourged mankind— typhus, cholera, yellow fever—have been brought under control by international teamwork. Better medical attention keeps more babies alive and prolongs the life span. Antiseptics, penicillin, DDT, what corner of the planet have they not reached? (Less attention has been given to the birth rate.)

On the other side of the ledger, the exhaustion of natural resources, water shortages, pollution, smog-stifled cities, traffic deaths and jams, the man on the belt, are also due primarily to applied science. These losses are all dwarfed, furthermore, by the threat of intercontinental missiles and radiation damage to human genes. More life or more death —applied science is impartial in its gifts, and the culture can bend decision either way. What no modern culture can do is to follow Samuel Butler's advice and throw our clocks and watches over the housetops. We might be blasted back to the simple life, but it is far too late deliberately to march back.

The generalist may have been perplexed by the gulf between classical theories in economics and tangible economic behavior, but this is nothing to the gulf between the profound effects of applied science on the behavior of nearly everyone alive, and the popular ignorance of science. The gulf appears to be growing deeper, as technical findings become more specialized and harder for the layman to follow. Let him try wiring an electronic computer, for instance, or even taping it.

THE CLOCKWORK UNIVERSE
Early in this book we compared models of the universe as

different ages saw it. Let us return for a moment and look again at the seventeenth century, when the great scientific revolution began, following the work of Copernicus and Galileo.

Experiments and research were going on in many fields. The idea of experimentation became a vogue; older authorities were everywhere challenged. Listen for instance to William Gilbert, physician to Queen Elizabeth I, and a pioneer in British medicine: "Very many philosophers making no investigation themselves, unsupported by any practical experience . . . make no progress by their records, and do not see what light they can bring to their theories, but their philosophy rests simply on the use of certain Greek words, or uncommon ones. . . ."

Today we call this the logical fallacy of "footnoting" or gobbledygook; Gilbert, in 1600, would have none of it.

Instruments were improved, experimental results were quantified, navigation became a science under the pressure of the early explorers. By 1650, when the Royal Society was founded in England, curiosity about the world outside was too vigorous and widespread to be held in the old cultural molds of theology and philosophy. Strong new winds were blowing. Descartes exclaimed: "Give me extension and motion and I will construct the universe!" Presently Newton, with his principles of gravitation, seemed to have done just that.

Members of the Royal Society thought in terms of absolutes. "Absolute, True and Mathematical Time," said Newton in the Principia, "of itself and from its own nature, flows equably without regard to anything external, and by another name is called Duration." Absolute Time, Absolute Space, Absolute Force, Causation, Matter—all were regarded as tangible realities, not just convenient concepts. The medieval essences which were supposed to compose the cosmos —Water, Fire and the rest—were replaced by an immense and orderly clockwork universe, theoretically capable, if one kept at his observations and calculations, of being completely known.

The Royal Society had broken out of the pseudo science of the Middle Ages, established the primacy of experiment, and made enormous advances in useful knowledge. But the theoretical balance swung too far; scientists overcompensated for the looseness of their predecessors by assuming a mechanical exactitude which was not there.

Many intelligent laymen today, when they think of "science," still envisage the clockwork universe, rigid and implacable. Writers elaborate upon this antiquated model to picture the state of the world in 1984, or some other future date when scientists have finally succeeded in reducing mankind to automata. Modern science, however, is off in a very different direction.

RELATIVITY AND PROBABILITY

It was Einstein who shattered the clockwork universe in 1904, as we have seen. With his first treatise on relativity, he joined space and time and broke up the absolutes of Newton with as much finality as Newton had broken up the medieval essences of Fire, Air and Water. Einstein did not prove that Newton was wrong, only that his equations did not fit the whole universe; new principles were needed for the galaxies. Relativity was met with great skepticism by scientists as well as laymen, but as the experimental data came in, and as matter was only too obviously converted into energy in the fission of an atomic bomb, the scientific world to a man accepted Einstein.

If the generalist wants really to understand relativity and modern science generally, he may begin by learning the theory of sets, calculus and probability, and so become something of a specialist. I recommend such a course highly, but it lies beyond our present scope. The idea of knowledge in terms of relationships, however, is very much in order, and indeed is central to this entire book. Einstein's approach spread rapidly through the natural sciences and presently into the behavioral sciences. Under the old Absolutes, a bad boy was a bad boy. Full stop. But now the social scientist asks: What about his glands? What about his family? What about the street gang from which he derives his values?

Scientists are thinking in terms of *process*, where an effect may arise from many causes, and in turn induce more causes, in an endless spiral. They are thinking in terms of *structure*, by which they mean the relations of parts to wholes. They have substituted *probabilities* for absolute laws and principles. No law in advanced science today is regarded as 100 per cent so—though many things may be 99.999 per cent—close enough for practical purposes. Every important advance in science brings us closer to the perfect fit, but scientists do not expect ever to find that ultimate equation.

By abandoning absolutes, scientists stand on the firmest ground in their history, as attested by the rush of new knowledge and invention in both physical and social sciences. Probabilities in physics are likely to be higher than probabilities in anthropology, but physics has been around longer.

Meanwhile how is the generalist to thread his way through the whole confusing maze? Obviously he cannot know all about "science," even if in his professional life he has a scientific specialty, such as genetics or nuclear physics. Obviously he should avoid the suspicion and mysticism often felt by the man on the street. The generalist, I think, should follow important new discoveries in scientific research, even spending a good deal of time to understand their significance. These are knowledge of the world we live in, contributions to all mankind. If he understands the scientific attitude, the generalist may even practice it in solving many personal problems.

OUTTHINKING A CROW

Here is a homely illustration of the universal use of primitive science. Some years ago I became annoyed with the way crows were stealing our garden corn; no scarecrow de-

terred them. I watched them pull up seedlings, then take off
at an angle. Would a kind of cat's cradle of stakes and string
bother the take-off, causing them to hit a wing as they rose?
It required only a few minutes to test the theory by driving
some stakes and stretching a ball of string back and forth
across our corn patch.

Observation seemed to show the theory was working, but
crows are smart. For a controlled experiment, I planted some
corn outside the protected area. In a few days it was gone.
I asked neighbors to try the invention; it worked for them,
and the theory grew stronger still. Mr. Crow obviously did
not like to operate under those strings.

For eight years now no corn has been stolen. I am not
justified in concluding that a wily old crow may not someday take a chance, only in concluding that my method has a
high probability of being effective. Meanwhile I had followed, quite unconsciously, the three steps in the scientific
method, observation, hypothesis and experimental verification. This kind of simple, practical science is a universal
legacy, common since the early Stone Age.

Writers on scientific method usually identify the following
sequence:

First, curiosity, an itch to know or solve something, which
causes one to observe and gather available facts. Specialists
comb the literature for papers already published which bear
on the problem. (I read no literature, but looked at crows
with a fresh and angry eye.)

Second, the formation of a theory to generalize the gathered
facts.

Third, the verification of the theory in such form that impartial observers can repeat and confirm. If confirmed, the
theory can then be used to *predict.*

Knowledge goes forward even when a theory fails of con-
firmation. "Well," says the lab man, "we don't have to fool
around with *that* hypothesis any more; let's get going on this
one." Finding out what isn't so can sometimes be as important as finding out what is.

WHAT IS "SCIENCE"?

In English "science" is a broad term with a number of meanings, running from the "science" of boxing to quantum theory. Philosophy and theology are sometimes called sciences. The *scientific attitude,* however, can be used to limit the field. The scientific attitude includes a quest for facts, and takes a kind of tough satisfaction in following them whatever the cherished cultural patterns they may collide with.

Karl Pearson, in *The Grammar of Science,* defines it as follows:

> Now this is the peculiarity of the scientific method, that when once it has become a habit of mind, that mind converts *all* facts whatsoever into science. The field of science is unlimited; its material is endless, every group of natural phenomena, every phase of social life, every stage of past or present development, is material for science. The unity of all science consists alone in its method, not in its material. The man who classifies facts of any kind whatever, who sees their mutual relation and describes their sequence, is applying the scientific method, and is a man of science.

This is broad enough for any generalist. It comprehends both the how and the why in scientific method, as well as every objective study, whether in the natural or social sciences. Max Planck emphasized the same idea when he said: "Actually there is a continuous chain from physics to chemistry to biology and anthropology, and thereon to the social and intellectual sciences, a chain which cannot be broken at any point."

A considerable group of critics hold that because a scientist tries to be objective, he places himself beyond ethical considerations. On the contrary, scientists have a rigorous code of ethics. Says P. W. Bridgman: "The fact has always been for the physicist the one ultimate thing from which there is no appeal, and in the face of which the only possible attitude is a humility almost religious." [1]

---

[1] *The Logic of Modern Physics* (Macmillan, 1932).

Most physicists were shocked when Einstein amended
Newton, but as the experiments confirmed relativity, they
had to follow the truth wherever it led. In what other human
activity is there a more compelling honesty?

Earlier we told of the archaeologists in Europe, who helped
to push back the accepted age of the earth by some millions
of years. One of the diggers, Dr. Rigollet of Amiens, gives us
a moving example of the honesty of a scientist. He so vigor-
ously objected to the conclusions of de Perthes, that he organized an expedition to St. Acheul to conduct his own
excavations, prove de Perthes wrong, and restore the authority of the Biblical account. Says Bibby: "But as Rigollet
turned up specimen after specimen of the hand axes and
other tools that now go by the name of Acheulian, he gradually became convinced that de Perthes was right. When in
1854 he published his report, he came out squarely on the
side of his erstwhile opponent."

Here is another example, a century later, which interests
me particularly as a writer. A famous journalist visits a clinic
to get a story on juvenile delinquency. A psychologist on the
staff uses a hypothetical case to illustrate one phase of the
clinic's activity. The journalist incorporates this dramatic
case in his story as a true experience. When the psychologist
objects, the writer grows angry, and the trustees of the clinic,
eager for publicity, urge the psychologist to play along.

What should the psychologist do? His duty is absolutely
clear, and is spelled out in the Code of Ethics of the American Psychological Association. "The psychologist may be expected to offer every assistance to reputable reporters, but
he may refuse to give materials to a reporter who does not
adhere to the ethical standards of the profession." The psychologist killed the article as written.

"EGGHEADS" AND "LONGHAIRS"

The following section applies particularly to the United
States, but it may have some elements of useful knowledge
for generalists elsewhere. Incidentally, the flat contradiction

in the two popular terms—egghead and longhair—is a good indication of the confusion present.

When I was in public school near Boston many years ago, I was careful not to rank too high in my class for fear of being called "teacher's pet." The scholastic pecking order put athletes at the top, dullards at the bottom, and bright children along in the middle, provided they did not flaunt their brightness. Later, at college, football players were still supreme, but the penalty for intelligence was less severe—though if one spent too much time at his books he might be called a "greasy grind."

This downgrading of learning has been chronic in America for a long time, though the founding fathers were never touched by it. It seems to have come in with large waves of immigration. Mark Twain was terrified of being thought an intellectual, as much of his writing, especially *Innocents Abroad,* shows. Henry Adams despaired of his country, and Henry James moved to England to write his novels. A low point was reached in the McCarthy era of the 1950's, when anyone with ideas was suspected of being an agent of Moscow. The Senator from Wisconsin, like Bishop Landa in Yucatán four centuries earlier, presided over the burning of books—including some of my own.

An opinion survey by Purdue University representing eight million high-school students in 1956, showed the following reactions to science and scientists:

30 per cent of the students thought a scientist could not be a normal family man.

27 per cent thought that scientists were willing to sacrifice the welfare of others to further their own interests.

25 per cent thought scientists were queer.

14 per cent thought they were definitely evil.

9 per cent thought it impossible for a scientist to be honest.

Could the familiar advertising copy of men in white coats, peering through microscopes, and endorsing dubious concoctions under the caption "Science Says," have helped along the last two reactions?

A study made by Opinion Research Corporation for *Life* magazine in 1957 covers the ideas of adult Americans about scientists, and shows no improvement as compared with the high-school population. Only 10 per cent could name as many as two living scientists; some 30 per cent doubted if scientists could be trusted with scientific secrets; one-tenth believed every scientist is likely to be a spy, while great numbers pictured them as "old men with long hair and whiskers, who may be geniuses but are half insane."

Both the Purdue and the *Life* figures reflected the norms of the American culture at the time they were taken, a norm unique in the civilized nations of the world. A great debate followed in press, TV and radio as to how education, especially scientific education, should be reconstructed to meet the Russian challenge. The idea of reconstructing it for its own sake, and the sake of the young people of America, was not so often mentioned.

What would generalists like to see taught about science in the schools of America—and elsewhere for that matter— in the age of the atom? Many readers may pause to review gaps in their own schooling, and prepare suggestions. Here are mine:

1. The broad history of science could be taught with its fascinating stories of discovery and exploration, from the invention of the wheel to the first rocket to the moon. Then some dramatic stories of great scientists and teams of scientists, such as Dr. Gorgas wiping out yellow fever during the building of Panama Canal. How the laws of science proceed from the specific to the more general, and the difference between looking for the *how* and the *why*.

2. The scientific attitude might be developed by conducting simple experiments (illustrating the idea of controlled experiments) in the classroom, the field, the home, in mat-

ters related to the students' interests—motorcars, airplanes, cooking, electronics, satellites.

3. Mathematics should be studied along with science, as part of the language of science. The Carnegie Corporation of New York is promoting a new method which makes mathematics an adventure in straight thinking, rather than an endless series of manipulations to get the "right answer." Mathematics as taught in Europe and Russia today, as well as in the United States, has been on the wrong track for three hundred years.[2] This is the reason, says Peter Drucker (himself a product of the stiff Gymnasia of Austria), that all of us— except the "naturals"—forget everything we have learned a few months after the final examination.

The Carnegie experiments for high-school students begin with the *theory of sets*—any collection of things, events, ideas—and proceed from there to weave all the subjects, arithmetic, algebra, geometry, up to calculus, into a unified, closely related development, growing the way the mind grows, and hopefully remaining in the conscious memory as a permanent aid to logical thinking. A crash program to stuff children with more drilling in manipulation will do nothing whatever, says Drucker, to transform the United States, or any other society, into a mathematically literate nation. Mathematics is a language of order, relations, logical progression, $x = f(n)$, but this grand concept is seldom taught, either here or abroad.

4. The "naturals" in mathematics, and gifted students generally, must be identified, as in Russia, and given all the education they can absorb, right through postgraduate work if they can take it, by government scholarship when unable to pay their own way. It has been estimated that we waste half the brains of America by not planning and financing educational opportunity for higher education.

---

[2] Article in *Harper's Magazine,* April, 1958.

If we compare the ancient myths about the cosmos, including all their poetic imagination, with the universe as it now unfolds before the two-hundred-inch telescope, we cannot fail to be stirred by the incomparably grander view from Mt. Palomar. This, too, every generalist, as well as Alan and other young people, should come to see.

20. What About Religion?

MANY GENERALISTS will subscribe to one or another of the world's great religions. Some will be humanists or agnostics. I do not think that any will be belligerent atheists, fundamentalists of any sect, or devout Communists or Fascists. A generalist is wary of rigid dogma in any form. He cannot insist on the superiority of his own faith over all other faiths, but accepts the fact that faith is a type of universal behavior, found in every culture. He will look for useful knowledge about religion, therefore, in two broad areas:

First, objective studies of the several religions, comparing their history and observances.

Second, a study of standards of conduct in various societies, hoping to find a basis here for an ethical system acceptable to all societies.

I shall only glance briefly at the first, but the reader may delve more deeply in some specialized work on comparative religion. The second approach is relatively new, chiefly the work of cultural anthropologists, and to this we will give more attention. The United Nations has been working on a universal Bill of Rights, an experiment in universal ethics. As the world moves toward technological unity, we need such a code even more than a common language. First another word, however, about that continuing semantic con-

flict of "science versus religion." It is not so lively as in the
days of Thomas Huxley and Bishop Wilberforce. ("Were you
descended from a monkey on your mother's side or your
father's?") But the conflict is still with us, and will be for
quite a while.

RELIGION AND SCIENCE

Many scientists—Father Mendel, Jeans, Millikan, for example, as well as Dr. Rigollet—have been devout and con-
scientious church members. Many others, while not com-
municants, cherish a private faith. "I am using religion,"
writes Julian Huxley, "to denote an overall relation between
man and his destiny, and one involving his deepest feelings,
including his sense of what is sacred." Bridgman, we recall,
speaks of the humility of the physicist before the fact, as a
feeling "almost religious." The obligation to render a true
report, accurate within carefully stated limits, is more bind-
ing on a scientist than on priest or layman.

Edward Sapir draws a distinction between "religion" and
"a religion." The latter includes a church, officials who guard
its rituals, canonical traditions which have grown up around
sacred texts, alleged to have been revealed by God, or the
gods, and faithfully set down by the founder. A formal religion with appropriate texts appears only in highly developed
cultures.

Religion without the "a" in front of it, says Sapir, "is man's
never-ceasing attempt to discover a road to spiritual serenity
across the perplexities and dangers of daily life." This road
is not the road of science, and only an incurable optimist
will try to identify such a feeling with the curiosity, the craving to know, of a scientist. A devout scientist, however, who
has at the same time a deep love of nature, may privately
reconcile the two roads.

Sapir makes a further distinction between evangelical and
ritualistic religions. The former seeks an intense emotional
experience for the individual, while the latter tends toward
a settled orthodoxy with a formal body of ritual. "One might

teach Protestant revivalism to a Blackfoot or a Sioux; a Zuñi would smile uncomprehendingly." Zuñis have been settled on their milpas for centuries and prefer a dignified ritual.

The scientific method as such is called amoral, but as Alexander Leighton observes, ethics may enter a given piece of research at three points: (1) when a scientist decides *what* to investigate—say segregation in the schools; (2) when he selects techniques for carrying on the investigation—for example, in rejecting certain surgical experiments on human beings; and (3) when he decides how to apply the results—say whether or not to manufacture a new drug. Ethical considerations appear furthermore in the whole scientific method, as Hayakawa points out: "Science, which is the accumulation of informative statements, although claiming not to deal with values, is itself based on some of the most general values in existence, such as the preference for truth over error, for generality over the cataloguing of unrelated data, for intellectual cooperation over concealment and secrecy." [1]

THE GREAT RELIGIONS

Membership in the great religions of the world today is estimated as follows:[2]

	Millions of persons
Roman Catholic	484
Orthodox (Greek Catholic)	129
Protestant	209
Total Christian	822
Moslem (Islam)	417
Hindu	319
Confucian	300
Buddhist	150
Taoist	50
Shinto	30
Jewish	12
	2,100

[1] *ETC*, Autumn, 1949.
[2] *Information Please Almanac*, 1958.

These figures are rough estimates, but they bring out some interesting points. The religions of Asia and the East account for 1,300 million persons, compared with 800 million Christians, mostly in Europe and the Americas. Judaism, in spite of the very considerable attention it receives, accounts for only 12 million members today, and never has had more than a tiny fraction of the total religious community. If one adds its derivatives, Christianity and Islam, however, the total comes to a billion and a quarter individuals influenced by monotheism through the Jehovah of the Jews.

Formal religious systems began with sun worship and worship of nature generally, including sacred animals. Egyptians thought highly of the cat, the Maya of its wild relative, the American tiger. Later might come a pantheon of assorted gods. Early cults practiced blood sacrifice, ceremonial cannibalism and other horrid rites. Self-perpetuating groups of priests controlled religion even more effectively than self-perpetuating boards of directors now control large corporations. How the rank and file participated in these primitive religions, except as devout members of the congregation, we do not know.

Then came a curious and significant development. Spanning a relatively limited period of less than a thousand years, from about 300 B.C. to 600 A.D., five great world religions were launched, four of them in Asia; they attained mass followings, and diffused over the planet:

> Buddhism in India, about 300 B.C.
> Hinduism in India, succeeding Buddhism, about 200 B.C.
> Confucianism in China about 100 A.D.
> Christianity in Europe (Council of Nicaea) about 300 A.D.
> Islam in Arabia about 600 A.D.

Buddhism spread to Ceylon, Burma, China, Tibet, Korea and Japan. Christianity conquered the Roman Empire, surged over all the continents, but especially Europe and the Americas. Islam overflowed from Arabia into Africa,

Asia, Indonesia, and over islands in the South Pacific. Diffusion among the great religions was marked. Hinduism was a direct outgrowth of Buddhism; the Koran proclaims both Jesus and Abraham as true prophets. Religions also competed with one another and still do—sometimes violently, in holy wars and crusades; thousands died in recent clashes between Moslems and Hindus in India.

All the great religions have split and resplit into sects, which have often showed less tolerance for one another than for competing faiths. Even the Jews, whose relative solidarity has been phenomenal, now have several divisions in Israel, as well as orthodox and liberal synagogues in the United States. In Biblical times they were divided between Judah and Israel.

Protestants divide into major sects, such as Baptist, Methodist, Presbyterian, which in turn divide into subsects—such as General Baptists (55,000 members), Primitive Baptists (72,000), United Baptists (64,000), Free Will Baptists (164,000), National Baptist Evangelical Life and Soul Saving Assembly of the United States of America (58,000), and many more. Roman Catholics, too, have a few splinter groups, such as the North American Old Roman Catholic Church (84,000), and the Polish National Catholic Church of America (250,000); but the Holy See in Rome holds them all loosely together.

COMPARATIVE RELIGION

Comparative religion as an academic study began at the time of the Crusades with polemics against Islam, but since then it has grown more impartial and scientific. Religions are analyzed the way political systems are analyzed, with a strong effort to eliminate bias. C. J. Ducasse, formerly president of the American Philosophical Association, observes:

> A person ... realizes that if he had been born and brought up in a different part of the world, his religion would almost automatically have been the one that happened to prevail in that particular region. And this thrusts upon him the question

whether the location of a man's birthplace determines not
merely which religion he will believe, but also its truth or
falsity. . . . The various religions . . . moreover . . . can be
used otherwise than in the beneficent manner that gives them
worth. . . . This forces on modern man's attention the fact
that the religions, like the sciences, are ambivalent and have
. . . to be carefully sifted.

In the nineteenth century translations appeared of the
sacred books of Indian, Persian, Chinese and other religions,
and movements arose in Europe based upon them. Annie
Besant in England, for example, wove various Oriental fea-
tures into her cult of Theosophy. Today, some Western intellectuals, especially psychiatrists, are interested in Zen Buddhism, a subsect originating in Japan. The late Dr. Pratt of
Williams College went so far as to say that "there are two
kinds of cultured people: those who have read Professor
Suzuki's work on Zen Buddhism, and those who have not."
The deciphering of the Dead Sea Scrolls is throwing a good
deal of light—to some fundamentalists an alarming amount
—on the genesis of Christianity.

Specialists have found many similarities among the great
religions. "Confucius," says Professor George Hedley, "would
have been quite at home sitting among the wise men who
compiled the book of Proverbs, and Laotse would have said
of the Logos of the Fourth Gospel, 'This is just what I mean
by the Tao.'" Along with ritual, the great religions have
formulated rules of ethical behavior which often parallel one
another, such as the Golden Rule of Confucius, the Noble
Eight-Fold Way of the Buddhists, and the Ten Command-
ments of Jews and Christians.

IS COMMUNISM A RELIGION?

Communism has been called a religion, as noted earlier,
and various parallels are obvious. There is a founder, Karl
Marx, with a revered text, *Das Kapital*, which disciples never
tire of expounding by chapter and verse. There is a hagiology
of saints and martyrs, such as Lenin, Engels, Rosa Luxem-

burg. (Stalin seems at the moment to have been defrocked.) The zealous consecration among the faithful is almost monastic in its renunciation of luxury and pleasure, not to mention the total suppression of a sense of humor.

But here the parallel ends. The great religions are founded on love, Marxism is largely founded on hate—hate of the capitalist, the rich, the bourgeoisie, the imperialist.

PLANETARY ETHICS

We remember the saying that "if God did not exist He would have to be invented." As we look at the uncertainty and mystery of all human life, at the suffering, bewilderment and tragedy endured by the peoples of the world since the ice ages, we realize the strength of their longing for a hand to hold on to, a hand stronger than their own. Medical science has reduced some of the pain, but bewilderment and tragedy loom more stark than ever. The need too for a universal, planetary ethic was never more urgent.

We have mentioned the Cross Cultural Survey at Yale, in which anthropologists have catalogued the customs and belief systems of many varied societies. If one is interested in marriage customs around the world, for instance, he will find them summarized under *M*, tribe by tribe, from Australian Bushmen to the Zuñi. Professor G. P. Murdock and his associates, working from the Survey, have listed the customs which are found in every society so far analyzed. A sampling of this list shows the following universal customs and attitudes, many with a heavy moral content, and all of them controlling behavior:

CUSTOMS COMMON TO ALL SOCIETIES

Language	Trading and exchange
Number system	Toolmaking
Personal names	Medicine complex
Calendar	Faith healing
Kin groups	Food taboos
Marriage rites	Cleanliness rules

Funeral rites	Religious ritual
Incest taboo	Soul concepts
Pregnancy usages	Mythology
Puberty rites	Cosmology
Modesty about natural func- tions	Divination
Government and law	Interpretation of dreams
Penal system, (covering mur- der, rape, theft, false wit- ness, for members of the in-group)	Luck superstition Weather control (by prayer and magic) Dancing (often highly ritu- alistic)
Status system	Decorative arts
Population policy	Games
Property rights	Athletic sports
Inheritance rules	Gift giving
Co-operative labor systems	Hospitality rites

All around the world, since man became man, these customs and patterns have appeared in the culture of *every known society*. Sometimes they are heavily elaborated and accented, sometimes anthropologists find only a trace. They are never quite identical and always slowly changing. Here in this table lies the true heritage of Homo sapiens, the things he has been universally concerned with. It is a reality not to be found in popular ideas about the club-swinging caveman, or the noble savage, or original sin. Nor is it found in the belief system of any single nation or any organized religion.

Anthropologists are fond of saying that some do and some don't, but in this list they all do. It is impossible to inspect the items carefully without realizing again how human similarities transcend human differences; how all men are brothers under the skin. From Chicago to the Congo, from Sydney to Kamchatka, there is a common way of life below the surface differences—a language to bind the band together, a closely woven family system, protection and training of children, hospitality, a system of government and law, toolmaking and trading, the arts, medicine, games, religion, cosmology—which turns into science. Though certain crimes are similar and everywhere penalized, feuds and organized warfare are not on Professor Murdock's list. Many tribes go to war, but the custom is not universal.

AT THE TOP OF THE WORLD

In 1956, a party of Swiss climbed Everest twice, also Lhotse, the fourth highest mountain in the world. Like all European expeditions they employed a small army of native porters as far as the base camp, and selected Sherpa guides for higher camps. Albert Eggler, who led the expedition, gives color to the above list of common traits when he says:

> . . . Wherever we went we met people who think and feel as we do ourselves. Their usages, their manners . . . were perhaps divorced from ours, but the differences tended to disappear, and the common unifying factors stood out, the more we had to do with them. The joys and sorrows which encourage and depress these people . . . are basically the same as those which shape our own action; and many of us developed a better understanding with some Sherpa and Lama than with many of our everyday friends. And we have all achieved a new approach to life through our contact with the people of Nepal, and their age-old culture and religion.[3]

The Swiss climbing team on starting home was received at the monastery of Thyangboche, almost fourteen thousand feet above the sea, by the robed lamas, seated according to rank. The native Sherpas filed past and touched the floor with their foreheads in front of the image of Buddha. After a period of complete silence the head lama began to pray, joined presently by the other lamas in a swelling chorus. One after another, they reached for their musical instruments, and the tones of the big conch blown by the head lama suddenly filled the room. Clarinets followed, then two long horns. Now one, now another instrument dominated with a solo in a curious rhythm, until they all joined in a thunderous fortissimo, which ended in a slow drum roll.

What could be a grander place for ritual than under the shoulder of the highest mountain in the world?

---

[3] *The Everest-Lhotse Adventure* (Harper, 1957).

SURVIVAL AS THE ULTIMATE TEST

The elements of a culture can be classified in various ways. I like to divide them into those which obviously promote survival, those which endanger it, and those which seem to be neutral. As a vigorous culture expands, it naturally tends to shed its antisurvival customs—such as the Hindu suttee. The United States is now in the process of trying to eliminate water pollution and soil erosion, after having pretty well eliminated such destructive earlier customs as child labor in factories and long hours for working women.

Most cultural traits are neutral, having little or no effect on community survival; but let no member of the society challenge them with impunity. There are penalties, of which the most severe may be ridicule. What American corporation executive, for instance, could face a hot and busy day in his corner office in a bathing suit? A potentate in the South Seas, however, might find such a costume quite appropriate.

Samples of all three sorts of traits—neutral, survival, and antisurvival—can be found in Murdock's list of common customs. If we combine the list with Mark May's seven wants of mankind as developed in Chapter 15, and with a list of cultural universals I once analyzed with the help of Ralph Linton,[4] we have the basis, I think, for a tentative statement of ethical practices common to all societies. Most people everywhere today, and as far as we can see into the past, tend to call these activities "good," and their reverse "bad," or at least unworthy of much attention. The reader is asked to check the following points with care; how far does he consider them "good"?

A TENTATIVE CODE OF COMMON ETHICS

Protection of the monogamous family, with training and security for children. A ban on incest, and the disapproval, though not outright denial, of divorce.

Protection of the natural environment, both living space and resources.

---

[4] Described in *The Proper Study of Mankind.*

Protection of physical and mental health through hygiene and medicine.

A just government, ultimately subject to the control of its members, with adequate protection of life and property, against murder, theft, etc.

Opportunity to improve living standards.

Open communication, unhindered travel. Opportunity to explore and find new knowledge. Research. Science.

Opportunity to worship without state interference and without interfering with the faith of other men.

Opportunity to develop the arts, the dance, music, design. In more sophisticated societies, architecture, sculpture, painting, literature, the theater, the ballet, symphonic music.

Opportunity for recreation—sports, games, hobbies. A chance to break down the arbitrary distinction between work and play.

To some readers this may seem but a common sense program, quite devoid of ethical considerations, except for the point concerning worship. To others, including your author, it is a kind of charter for the good life, and thus deeply concerned with ethics. The late A. Powell Davies, minister of All Souls' Unitarian Church in Washington, reflected, I believe, the opinion of many generalists when he said:

I do not think that morality depends upon any particular system of religious doctrine. . . . I think that spiritual values are inherent in ethical standards; also the basic faith that life is meaningful enough to make virtue its own reward. . . . What is needed is the identification of the spiritual and moral values in all the great provinces of religious culture (and outside them), so that the world may have a common basis for its united life.

This is what we have been searching for in the categories of the Cross Cultural Survey, a common standard of what is felt to be right and good, with broad survival value, for a human society high in the Himalayas, along the Volga, in the South Seas, on the Atlantic seaboard, or anywhere on earth.

21 . Footnote on the Arts

ART is a thorny subject to put in a general frame. Whatever one says about it is likely to be emotionally upsetting to the composure of this or that school; witness the battle over the work of the so-called abstractionists today. There are, however, several observations to be made which, I believe, constitute useful knowledge.

To begin with, let us go back to the quiz programs and Mr. Gallup's "cultural Olympics" with its fifty questions, discussed in Chapter 1. The quizzes never tire of asking: "Who wrote *Pagliacci?*" "Give titles of three novels by Dostoevski." "What great school of painting arose in France in the nineteenth century?"

Is this useful knowledge for the generalist? It has a kind of social utility as background for conversation at dinner parties, and it has an indirect value, if connected with true appreciation. Acquaintance with great works of art can give not only intense pleasure but a deeper understanding of life, people, the world. Let no generalist ever say I told him not to be concerned with art.

There is a difference, however, between *experience* of art, and knowledge about it. What the quiz programs test is the knowledge, and they can represent, moreover, a form of snobbery which is anti-art as surely as astrology is anti-knowledge. Bored audiences at concerts and operas help performers make a living, but do not help them perform well, or help the authors and composers convey their meaning. Such audiences are like a dead telephone line; no response comes back; it makes little difference what one tries to tell them.

One cannot of course know if he likes a play or symphony until he sees or hears it. Some sophisticated art forms need many exposures, the deliberate training of one's senses, and considerable patience. If one just pretends, if he is not honest about his impressions, he may never be rewarded with the intense experience which true appreciation brings.

A boyhood memory illustrates this intense personal experience. It came during a European trip that was intended to be instructive, broadening and "cultural." I had been taken through gallery after gallery, and lectured by a tour leader whose words meant so little that I wrote a cruel limerick about him. Then one August morning I saw the Hermes of Praxiteles, with its immortal grace and the patina of centuries on its mellow surface. It struck me like a blow; I daresay I staggered under the impact, with tears in my eyes. Praxiteles was saying something to me that I heard and understood, something about a familiar subject, the human body, my own body; and about an unfamiliar one, the unknown Greek boy, so long dead, who sat for the portrait of a god.

Since then I have had many similar experiences, though none more intense. I have learned to open my eyes in an art gallery and to open my ears at a concert, or alone with a Bach recording. I do not expect to enjoy everything at any gallery or any concert, but I am deeply grateful for one moving experience, for one flash of insight, as in that museum in Greece so long ago.

The reader may be indifferent to Praxiteles, but moved by Rembrandt, or Mozart, or Chinese paintings of the Tang dynasty. The experience is always personal and intimate. This is why there is no special body of knowledge about art

which can be recommended to the generalist. He must find
meaning for himself. He may have to search widely and
long, and above all he must be honest with himself. If a bell
does not ring he must admit it does not ring. Otherwise no
bells may ever ring for him.

After searching, the generalist will know what form of art
means most, and whether he wants to specialize to some
extent. The more he learns about it, the deeper and more
intense his appreciation will be, but as a generalist he also
knows the importance of a wider view and a wide receptive-
ness to a variety of forms.

Another way to increase awareness is through hobbies
and amateur expression. I draw cats in charcoal because I
love their graceful motion and the patterns on their fur. My
wife plays chamber music indefatigably. We do this solely
for our own enjoyment—though when people praise my
sketches I am not displeased. One summer at the shore both
of us splashed around with water colors—very bad ones, but
we learned to see new colors in sand and sky and water.

This sort of thing can have meaning, but no generalist,
as such, needs to memorize the names, dates and *chefs-
d'œuvre* of the world's artists, any more than those of the
world's scientists. As in the case of history, he may want to
make a special study of the arts of his native land, but such
a study by an American would hardly interest a generalist
from Japan, or even one from Sweden.

One thing the intelligent layman needs to remember is
the importance of arts and crafts on Professor Murdock's
list of universals, recited in the last chapter. Artistic expression is a concern of every society so far studied from the Old
Stone Age to date; an essential of the good life.

To carry the idea of universality one step further, there is
evidence for believing that the arts concern not only *some*
people in the society, but all normal individuals. There is
reason to believe that every one of us has a built-in drive to

create something beyond the level of sheer utility, and to appreciate it when created by others. The intensity of appreciation of course varies—probably on the frequency distribution curve.

The fact that some societies, such as the ancient Greeks and the Renaissance Florentines, have cultivated these drives, while others, like the Americans and the Australians, have tended on the whole to disregard them, is a matter of culture—in the strict anthropological sense. To use the old illustration, if a thousand Midwestern American babies could be miraculously transported to the Florence of the Medicis, we could expect many of them to become artists and craftsmen, all of them to appreciate the arts of the time. A miraculous transportation in the other direction, from Florence in 1500 to Kansas in 1900, would produce the Midwestern evaluations of matters of art at the turn of the century—evaluations now being rapidly replaced by more cosmopolitan ones.

REFERENTS FOR "ART"

Before going farther into "universality," let us set down as plainly as we can what we are talking about. The earliest art objects, unearthed by archaeologists, appear to be designs etched by a sharp stone on flint and bone tools. Later came designs on pottery, and on a far higher level, the cave paintings in France. Murals and bas-reliefs recently discovered in the Sahara may be older than the European cave paintings.

An examination of these and other activities makes it difficult to separate art from necessary function, especially in the matter of form. Is the exquisite shape of an Egyptian flint knife art or utility? Is the rain dance of the Zuñi functional or aesthetic? To ask the question is to answer it: obviously both; function and its elaboration are often inseparable. The two can be split verbally but not operationally. We have a parallel question very much with us today. Do the mass media produce art or only entertainment? Sometimes both—with Charlie Chaplin as an outstanding example.

We are talking about such elaborations of function and expression as:

The work of craftsmen	The dance
The design of tools and utensils	Music
Architecture, from Ur on	The pageant and theater
Sculpture	Legend and poetry
Drawing and painting	Written literature

These arts can be divided into two grand classes, those that serve communication between man and man, those that serve a sense of form and design. A creative artist without an audience is like a speaker without a listener. It is quite normal, however, to shape and design things in a form pleasing to the one who shapes them, regardless of audience. In a moment I will cite a personal example.

A work of art may communicate a feeling, a sharp association from the files of memory, an aspect of nature, which gives fulfillment and makes life more worth the living. It can orient one more closely to his own culture, or serve as a bridge between different cultures and different ages, for a work of art takes on a kind of immortality.

When the diplomats and politicians make no progress toward peace, the musicians, the painters and storytellers may perhaps break through the armed frontiers. A Moscow audience in the spring of 1958 cheered to the echo a young American pianist from Texas who won a musical contest, one that Russians follow as Americans follow the World Series in baseball. Reporters said the audience was delighted to hear an American playing Tchaikovsky so well, and to realize that Americans, like themselves, value serious music and skillful performance. A vital message had penetrated the Iron Curtain.

The final outcome of the battle between so-called abstract

art and a graphic form which portrays something recognizable will be determined by the above-mentioned principle of communication. Will abstractions say enough things to enough people to survive? If there is no communication except color and design, people will stop buying canvases when the present fashion is over, and go back to buying rugs. If there is widespread communication, abstract painting and sculpture will endure, with queues at the doors of museums in 1984. We shall have to wait and see, for no amount of critical verbiage is going to settle it. Meanwhile the generalist, as such, may as well avoid the scrimmage.

EVERYONE AN ARTIST

This part of our discussion might begin with a rock-bottom case from personal experience. It has to do with art on the most primitive level of form and order, the feeling inside an early craftsman.

When I tire of desk work, I often lay down my pencil for an ax and go up the back hill on my place for firewood. Such work is not repetitious, for every tree presents a different problem. Over the years I have come to recognize two competing impulses in such outdoor operations: one I have nicknamed "least work," the other "perfectionism." The first is akin to science, it seems to me, the second to art, and I can sit back, as it were, and watch the conflict with my conscious mind.

"Least work" affects every fresh operation I undertake, such as the dissection of a wild cherry tree. I begin with the ax, lay it down presently for the saw, and drop the saw for the big pruners, whichever accomplishes the task with the smallest expenditure of energy. It is not a matter of conscious planning, but of an almost automatic impulse. As I work, my efficiency steadily improves. One's organism seems to seek the easiest way, just as a worn footpath follows not the straightest line, but the most comfortable gradient.

Now the conflict enters. As the branches are lopped off, I throw them into a pile, later to be burned. I begin by

throwing them helter-skelter, but as the untidy mass grows
I begin to feel uneasy. At some point, "perfectionism" over-
whelms "least work"; I discard my tools, and repile the
brush in a rounded and orderly structure which looks "ship-
shape" and right. Reasoning about time lost cannot stop
this operation, which no one but myself is likely ever to see.

Out there on the back hill, the two drives are in constant
competition, and the task would be far less interesting without the conflict. Carry it to a level beyond woodcutting:
would a man feel uneasy after he had fashioned a satisfactory clay pot unless his hand smoothed its surface into
a more pleasing symmetry, unless he put a bit of decoration
on its border?

FIESTA IN OAXACA

One man, you say, or perhaps a few men have an inner
drive to elaborate function. But how does one explain the
Indians of Mexico, descendants of the Maya, Toltecs and
Zapotecs? Though they lost their leaders, their science,
mathematics and architecture four hundred years ago, their
superb craftsmanship lives on, now blended with elements
from Spain.

In a big fiesta, you will be warmed and excited by the
color and design. You will see pottery, silverwork, glassware,
lacquer, leatherwork, masks, textiles, made not for display,
but in the villages for villagers. Certain towns specialize in
one or another of the crafts, and nearly every person could
be called an artist. You will see a booth for old iron in the
fiesta market with reclaimed nails spread on the counter in
a fan design; old bottles grouped by size and color; a burro
coming into market with a sunburst design of reeds arranged
on either flank. It seems impossible for these people to
arrange anything without color and composition. In my book
on Mexico I give a firsthand description of the market at
Oaxaca during a fiesta where Indians have come from
villages a hundred miles around, an account which documents this observation. We must remember too that out of

this matrix evolved not only the superb sculpture, jewelry, gold filigree work, mural painting and architecture of the ancient Maya and Zapotec, but also Rivera, Orozco and other muralists, to form one of the great schools of painting in the contemporary world.

If millions of poor Indians in Mexico can be artists, why not millions of not-so-poor citizens along the Mississippi? Do the Indians have a special set of genes? Biology will not allow it. Indian culture has fostered the arts and crafts for three thousand years, while Americans have no such tradition. But there is nothing to prevent them from acquiring it. We can only conclude that the Hispano-Indian culture encourages an artistic sense which is possible for any society. Art like science is indigenous, and either can be advanced or neglected by the culture. Science, or at least technology, fares better north of the Rio Grande at the present time, the arts and crafts a good deal worse.

APPRECIATING THE ARTS

If every man is a potential artist, he must also be a potential critic or consumer. And indeed appreciation of the arts is cosmopolitan. One may not appreciate the language, religion, politics, table manners, or sanitary arrangements of alien peoples, but their folk arts have almost universal appeal. One thinks of Peruvian textiles, Persian rugs, Eskimo ivory, African carved ebony, Etruscan bronzes, the carved canoes of Trobriand Islanders, the masks of the Stone Age people of New Guinea. There are no names and dates here for a quiz show, only universal delight.

I find an interesting variation in this process. Appreciation begins with:

Craftwork, which pleases nearly everybody. A lama from Tibet will be as delighted with the ruby tints of Sandwich glass—made a century ago on Cape Cod in Massachusetts to a formula now lost—as will an Indian from Oaxaca.

The *folk dances* of other cultures delight nearly everybody. Some sadistic ones need editing for Western taste.

Noble *architecture,* whether that of Babylon, Karnak, Angkor, Uxmal, Chartres, or the San Francisco bridges, has universal appeal.

Sculpture is not far behind. I happened to be at Teotihuacán near Mexico City with a New York artist when he suddenly saw the façade of serpents' heads below the Pyramid of the Sun, carved perhaps three thousand years ago. The man was stunned: "It's the finest thing I ever saw," he shouted. "It's the finest thing in the world!" That was the way he felt for the moment.

Painting and drawing—Japanese prints, Chinese painting, the murals of many lands, Leonardo, El Greco, Van Gogh. Says Cézanne:

> Our canvases are the milestones of Man—from the reindeer on the walls of caves to the cliffs of Monet—from the hunters, the fishermen who inhabit the Tombs of Egypt, the comical scenes of Pompeii, the frescoes of Pisa and Siena, the mythological compositions of Veronese and Rubens, from all these the same spirit comes down to us. . . . We are all the same man.

To me, the above list suggests a theory of aesthetic appreciation, which specialists may or may not accept. The items listed are all graphic and plastic arts, coming to us through light waves to the eye. The crafts are the most readily communicated, highly sophisticated painting probably the least.

With music, we enter a new dimension, sound waves coming to the ear. Appreciation is more difficult between cultures, and universality suddenly shrinks. Watching and hearing the Gamelan Orchestra from Bali, with its glittering décor and child dancers, the Westerner's eyes are delighted, but his ears are baffled if not repelled by the gongs and drums. Much of the music of Asia sounds like monotonous whining to the Western ear. How does Beethoven sound to a sophisticated Siamese? There is now a symphony orchestra in Tokyo, but do the Japanese really enjoy what they hear?

Literature presents an even more formidable barrier. The rhythm of the spoken ballad has some appeal, but written words encounter the difficulty of translation, as noted earlier. Great writing is a function of a given language, and many of the overtones which make it great cannot be expressed in another language. We have already quoted Robert Frost: "Poetry is what gets lost in translation." Is Albert Camus' *The Plague* the same book to a German or an American that it is to a native of France? Can Gogol's *Dead Souls* mean to anybody else what it means to a Russian? Could a reader not brought up in America really understand Jim in *Huckleberry Finn*—not only Jim's dialect, but his tragedy? Says Carlos Baker: "Much that belongs to the essence of a nation's common life seems to drop silently out of a novel, a play, or a poem, when it moves out of its native land into foreign climes." [1]

IN SUMMARY

Useful knowledge for a generalist in the field of art assumes that all human beings are potential artists, and one who believes this should seize every opportunity to find where his talent lies. No over-all rules can be laid down, everyone must find it for himself.

Everyone is not only a potential producer but a potential consumer, though appreciation across cultures seems to flow more easily in the graphic arts than in literature with its translation difficulties. Ordinary statements translate readily enough, and scientific papers present no such problem as *Huckleberry Finn,* for they can be cast, in part at least, in the universal language of mathematics.

In the arts, mankind finds a powerful force toward internationalism, one which UNESCO is trying hard to cultivate.

---

[1] *New York Times,* December 29, 1957. Translation loses less *inside* a language family—such as the Indo-European family. That is, an Englishman will get more out of a translation of Dante than out of a translation of Confucius.

When we Americans become thoroughly exasperated with the politicians in the Kremlin, let us remember the superb performances of the Moscow Art Theater, the incomparable ballerina Galina Ulanova, the three great modern composers, Prokofiev, Shostakovich, and Khachaturian, and one of the world's finest violinists, David Oistrakh. Let us remember the wild ovation in Moscow to a young pianist from Texas.

The politicians may shake their fists, the economists view with alarm, but artists, like scientists, know no frontiers.

22 . Calling All Generalists

WE BEGAN this book by asking what sorts of knowledge are more useful to the intelligent layman than the answers to most quiz programs. What will my grandson Alan need to know, or to have on ready call, by the time he reaches maturity? Another title for our survey might be: *How Not to Win $64,000.*

I have used "generalist" throughout as the equivalent of "intelligent layman," and I regard most laymen as intelligent. I have tried to show that man has a bigger and better brain than he normally uses, and that this is one of the mysteries of biology and evolution. Whatever its origin, it is high time we employ the great gift closer to capacity. Stuffing our memory files with loose facts is little better than accumulating anti-knowledge. It is in the searching out of variables and relationships that one begins to find wisdom.

Every year a great army of children arrives in the schools of the world without fixed ideas or serious prejudices, eager to know and understand. Gradually their parents, their teachers, their elders, narrow, if not altogether extinguish, this fresh curiosity. Yet its constant renewal in an annual supply of six-year-olds may be humanity's greatest asset— a wellspring from which a sounder wisdom and judgment may someday flow. The wisest teacher I know is wise because she listens to children.

A former student at Columbia sued the university for $7,016.[1] He alleged that he had been misled into believing that Columbia would teach him "truth, understanding, integrity, enlightenment, justice, liberty, courage, honesty and critical judgment." From this resounding salvo Dean Chamberlain retreated in good order, asserting that "wisdom is not a subject that can be taught; Columbia never claimed to teach it. Wisdom is the hoped-for end product, which many seek and many fail to attain." What Columbia can teach, and to a degree does teach, is the background material helpful for the attainment of wisdom.

GRAND TOUR

We have been on an extended tour in the foregoing pages seeking background material. To me, at least, it has been an exciting adventure. It has given me renewed appreciation of the explorers, scholars and scientists who have put this useful knowledge on the record; a new respect for the human mind which not only has found so many dependable answers, but will not be stopped from seeking more. Along with this modest selection from the great map of learning, our survey has noted various blank areas, terra incognita which may or may not someday be filled. Are there intelligent beings on planets outside the solar system? is, for instance, a question which will be very difficult to answer.

Trying to look at Homo sapiens with a certain detachment in relation to his environment helps to define his limits, as well as his astonishing capabilities. We have seen how our earth probably was born in a cosmic cloud of dust and gas; where, if not how, life began in the warm shallow seas; how all living things, including man, evolved over the eons by natural selection, modified by sudden mutations, and how the ice ages presented our ancestors with the challenge of using their wits to survive, or becoming another interesting

---

[1] *New York Times,* December 14, 1957.

biological experiment which failed. The planning necessary to trap a mammoth was similar in kind, if not degree, to the planning necessary to put a satellite in orbit.

It is highly probable that proto-man did not become true man until he had developed speech, and the apparatus for speech in brain, tongue, ear and vocal cords. Language was essential for expanding his mental powers, and made him the only creature on earth capable of complicated reasoning, ultimately to the point of a Copernicus and a Heisenberg.

We have noted that an individual without a group is as unthinkable as a group without individuals. Man is a social animal, and his character is molded by the culture of his society—its customs, belief systems and artifacts—as strongly as it is molded by his genes. We have seen in Professor Murdock's list that some seventy cultural traits, from calendar making to property rights, are shared by every society which anthropologists have studied. Cultures differ surprisingly, sometimes shockingly; but in the long view the similarities are more important than the differences. All groups can interbreed, and over the millennia have interbred in the course of vast migrations and countermarchings from the Caucasus to Easter Island. No large racial stock has been proved inferior to any other. Even the most primitive peoples have highly sophisticated language systems; but the characteristics of individuals within the stock follow the frequency distribution curve.

The spiral of culture began very slowly with the invention of fire tending and the first flint tools, but gradually gathered momentum like a compound-interest curve. Hunting peoples gave way to herders and then to the first cultivators of wheat, rice and maize. Settled living beside fields of grain developed irrigation systems and then, suddenly, came city walls, temples and a dawning civilization in the six centers of Mesopotamia, Egypt, India, China, Peru and Mexico.

That these centers developed largely independently indicates that a common pattern and a common drive are indigenous in the race.

With the first cities the spiral of culture began really to whirl! Civilization fosters specialized occupations, which foster more inventions—architecture, engineering, the arts, communication systems, writing, metalworking, religious rituals; invasions, conquests, and armaments; ships, caravans, trade routes, mathematics and philosophy. Presently came the first age of science in Greece, the One World of the Roman Empire, then Columbus and Magellan, the second age of science, as Copernicus removed man from the center of the universe. At last with Einstein came the dethronement of absolutes by probabilities, the proliferation of specialties and specialists; the threat and the promise of atomic power, the looming age of space.

OUT OF SCALE

One result of our survey in the foregoing chapters, especially as we contemplate the spiral of technology, is the extent to which specialists have distorted the environment of the world today and pulled human behavior out of scale. Generalists are needed in great numbers to offset what the specialists are doing to us. To put it in another way, we need more specialists equipped with wide perspective, to exert critical judgment on what they are doing as specialists. This, I take it, was Robert Oppenheimer's motive when he demurred about working on the hydrogen bomb; his general philosophy came in conflict with his expert knowledge. Almost everyone, as I said earlier, is both specialist and generalist; but the latter function has grown more and more neglected as specialties become more complex and demanding.

In *Fables for Our Time,* James Thurber imagines a conference of ostriches concerned with the loss of their ability to fly. One of them named Oliver complains that men can fly sitting down, while ostriches cannot fly at all. "The old ostrich glared at Oliver severely, first with one eye and then with the other. 'Man is flying too fast for a world that is round,' he said. 'Soon he will catch up with himself, in a great rear-end collision, and man will never know that what hit Man from behind was Man.' "

The old Indian on the Idaho reservation, cited earlier, and the old ostrich have much in common, while airplane designer Igor Sikorsky supports both. He is reported to have said that our planet is really too small for flying speeds of over five hundred miles an hour.

New York City seems to be hitting itself harder from behind every time I venture into its canyons and subways and rush-hour traffic. It has a kind of grandeur, and it shows what fantastic engineering problems specialists can overcome when they put their minds to it. But Megalopolis doesn't fit people; the specialists show little regard for biology. Among the new hazards is a dangerous increase of carbon monoxide during rush hours in New York.

An average man is 68 inches tall, and weighs 150 pounds. Impulses travel along his nerve fibers, probably in a binary on-and-off system, at not more than 200 miles an hour. Reactions slow up, furthermore, as he gets older. He can see and hear only so far, press only so hard, and hold only so much in his memory. Natural selection has fashioned him so, and despite the programs of the advanced eugenists there is not much prospect of changing this basic equipment for quite a while to come.

It is natural for critics, especially when they become grandfathers, to complain about speed, noise, traffic, change, the pace of modern life, and the disrespect of the young for their elders. These complaints have become standard; something like them has doubtless been heard in every culture since Mesopotamia. Today, however, they have a new validity. It is not only that the times are out of joint, and progress often out of scale with biology—the scale itself is going into a new dimension.

Just as the evolution of enzymes and later of photosynthesis and oxygen metabolism revolutionized the power of living organisms over the environment, so . . . technology . . . is revolutionizing it again. With his machines and processes, man advances his competitive position more in a century than he could in a million years of biological evolution. Because of his overwhelming competitive advantage, his numbers continue to increase prodigiously at the expense of other creatures. He threatens to sweep from the earth whole orders of life, and in doing so he may initiate irreversible changes that will sweep him off also. Man is fast outgrowing the planet.[2]

Everyone, the psychiatrists say, has his breaking point, and too many of us are now reaching it. Specialists, however, go merrily on making skyscrapers higher, smog thicker, traffic more impenetrable, and fall-out more lethal. Trips to the moon are brightly promised, but some ominous questions are unanswered. How, for instance, will the canals of the ear adjust to weightlessness?

Specialists bring down the death rate, which is humane, but leave the birth rate unchanged, thus causing the population curve to mount steeply. The generalist sees both ends of this process, and sometimes wonders if it might not be even more humane to follow nature's automatic regulation, in some respects, until the birth rate and the food supply can be brought into line.

Atomic power plants are fine, too, and every nation which can find the uranium is planning to build them, but nobody yet seems to know what to do with atomic wastes. The generalist wonders if it might not be wise to slow down on power plants until an answer to the problem of dangerous wastes is found, if it can be found. (Fusion plants, if ever developed, will not have this problem, it is said.)

When an up-and-coming real-estate man in Brooklyn advertises building lots for sale on the moon, we smile. But there is nothing to smile about in the following press report:

---

2 J. H. Rush, physicist, in *Saturday Review,* January 25, 1958.

"An American scientist speculated here yesterday that the Russians might one day be capable of freezing Florida or turning the Midwest into a permanent drought belt." It has also been proposed to spread lampblack over polar ice, melt off the ice caps, and raise the Atlantic Ocean a hundred feet or so, inundating Times Square. "Weather control," says H. T. Orville, reporting to President Eisenhower, "could have results more disastrous to the United States than atomic discoveries." [3]

Advertising is out of scale, and so are radio and TV commercials, and Sunday supplements. The biological sex drive is difficult enough to handle without having it stimulated on every hand by the mass media. The human senses and the human cortex are simply not equipped to deal with much of the world the specialists have rigged up for them.

This does not mean that hunters, farmers and handicraft civilizations were always in scale. The life of a galley slave was thoroughly abnormal, and so was the forecastle of Nelson's *Victory*. But we are experimenting with speeds, shocks and saturations which, as Dr. Rush says, are unprecedented. It is something like climbing in the Himalayas. If you are young and healthy you can go up to twenty-six thousand feet. Beyond that you cannot go; the legs won't lift, the mind won't focus. No human being has yet been found who can reach the top of Everest without an oxygen mask.

THINKING IN TERMS OF RELATIONS

Mankind is now experimenting with new ways of ordering his thoughts. His brain will be no keener than it was fifty thousand years ago, but the scientific attitude has given him ways and means to use it more effectively. This will tend to lessen diversities and widen common interests.

All men eat, but what food they eat, how they eat it, what kind of economy produces it, differ through time and place.

---

3 *New York Times*, January 28, 1958.

It is not the common fact of eating, but the *variables* which cause the trouble. The struggle between "Communism" and "capitalism" which now shakes the world is essentially a disagreement about the best way to get our food. The Communists demand state controls for accumulating the necessary calories, while the so-called free nations prefer action by individual enterprisers—modified to be sure by various state subsidies and regulations. Looked at from this viewpoint it seems a pretty silly question to divide us. It is man's tendency, says William C. Carleton, to raise relative values to the level of absolutes, and so produce human tragedies.

Today tragedy on the grand scale is in the air, and a vigorous use of relativity bitterly needed. Suppose a generalist were asked to participate in a conference to find methods of accommodation between East and West. Most extremists would refuse to attend. "You can't trust those Communists, so why waste your time?" is the word from the far Right. "You can't trust those capitalists," is the rejoinder from the Left.

The generalist cannot follow such rigid predetermined paths. He has to summon the variables which lie between the two extremes. Here are eleven propositions which, among others, he must bear in mind as he takes his seat:

1. Both the governments of the U.S. and the U.S.S.R. not only say they do not want war, but actually do not want war. It terrifies governments and peoples alike.

2. Both apparently agree that they do not want H-bombs in the hands of small nations—Egypt, Israel, Indonesia, Korea —thus providing a specific and urgent item for negotiation.

3. Russia and America were comrades in arms in 1917, and again in 1945.

4. They have no quarrel in respect to natural resources, for both are "have" nations.

5. They have no quarrel in respect to real estate, no Kashmir to fight about.

6. They have many international common interests. The control of outer space, Antarctica, weather control, atomic power for peace, the International Geophysical Year, and so on, are demanding joint action.

7. Many young scientists in Russia are growing bored with dialectical materialism.[4]

8. The "capitalist" countries are far along the road to the welfare state.

9. Russian rulers today have more in common with Peter the Great than with Marx and Lenin.

10. Russia and China may split. There are a number of possible real-estate rows in this quarter.

11. The cry that Communism is out to conquer the world has a familiar ring. Twenty years ago Hitler was out to conquer the world, and before that the Kaiser, and before that the British Empire. Walter Lippmann provides historical perspective when he says: "Islam and Christendom were at war for centuries. Neither conquered the other. Both have survived and flourished, and have managed to live in the same world. . . . My own view is that our struggle with the Communist powers is essentially like the wars of religion . . . it will never be finally settled, but it can be made to subside, and the rivalry can be held within tolerable limits."[5]

It is not easy to keep all these eleven facts and relations in mind, giving due weight to each. Only generalists can attempt it, as they come to the conference with open minds. The above is not so much a program for a current crisis, as an illustration of thinking in terms of relationships rather than absolutes. "There are many," says Lippmann, "who would assert that there is no part-way house between the surrender of the Communist powers and the defeat of the Western powers. They must yield to us, or we shall have to yield to them. . . . I do not believe that the world is as simple, as black and white, as all that." Nor does any generalist.

---

[4] See Reports of Russian Research Center at Harvard, of William Benton, John Gunther and others.

[5] *Look,* January 21, 1958.

When political leaders of both sides, however, do believe it, the chance of avoiding destruction grows less, and citizens sit watching helplessly as military technology carries us to a doom that a few years ago would have been incredible. Are we then to see the end of this little figure we have been tracing down the millennia, this superstitious, quarrelsome and creative being? Must he disappear from the planet before he has learned to use his mind at capacity?

Mankind will not be saved, I think, by trusting to luck, muddling through, or shifting responsibility to supernatural powers. The problem is ours, here and now, using the abilities we are endowed with, guided by useful knowledge which scholars and scientists have spread on the record, much of it quite recently. The times call for men and women who can read that record, act upon it, and lead us back into scale with our planet and our universe.

APPENDIX

A Quiz Program for Generalists

THERE HAS BEEN some criticism of the usual quiz program in the foregoing pages, and it seems only fair to suggest an alternative—an alternative with "whys" in it. Let us look at some sample questions—all covered in this book—that test awareness of things worth knowing for generalists.

It has been said that an educated person is one who knows what he does *not* know, and an uneducated person is one who knows all the answers. This is an overgeneralization, I am afraid, but an educated person does not hesitate to turn to a standard reference work, while an uneducated one often tries to bluff his way through by pounding the table. Or he just plain gives up, not knowing where to look for an answer.

So we will change the rules a little, and require for the following quiz that the generalist either give the answer off the top of his head, or tell how to go about looking it up. Furthermore his answer need not be correct down to the last decimal place, but reasonably correct. If he says, for instance, that the diameter of the earth is about 8,000 miles, he will not be disqualified because the correct figure happens to be 7,926 miles at the equator, and a quarter of a mile less from pole to pole. (As per the *Columbia-Viking Desk Encyclopedia.*) There are no trick questions in this quiz, only inquiries covering matters which generalists every-where should be familiar with:

1. How was our solar system probably formed?

2. How old is the earth?

3. Why did Copernicus shock and enrage his contemporaries?

4. How does natural selection work? Illustrate with a Flit gun case.

5. Why has natural selection ceased to work in the case of man?

6. What is the scientific evidence for unequal intelligence between the races of man?

7. If you encounter a chronically aggressive troublemaker what will you look for as probable causes?

8. What major characteristic sets man off from all other creatures?

9. What are some of the difficulties in a manned space flight?

10. Why do we have simultaneous discoveries in science?

11. What is the chief business of most modern states, as exemplified by their budgets?

12. What material condition makes civilization possible?

13. What do biologists mean by the "survival of the fittest"?

14. Why doesn't political democracy work in some Latin American countries, despite an excellent constitution?

15. What is the "managerial revolution," and why does it confound Marxism?

16. Is organized warfare found in all cultures? What do you deduce from your answer?

17. Are there any primitive languages? What do you deduce from that?

18. What are the three major policies to halt a business depression?

19. Can Russia have a business depression? Explain.

20. How do Russia and China finance armaments, new construction and capital goods?

21. Can the United States go bankrupt?
22. How does modern science differ from the "clockwork universe" of the Newtonian era?
23. Name three contributions to the knowledge of human behavior.
24. Explain the scientific attitude.
25. Why is science inseparable from ethics?

Answers in a moment. Observe that a number of them cannot be looked up in a reference book, for they constitute knowledge built in, not slot-machine answers. Question number 4, "How does natural selection work?" can be looked up, but it will be best to use a good one-volume encyclopedia; the big boys carry too much data for a short question. Question 11 about budgets can be answered from the *World Almanac*'s U.S. budget figures.

Mostly, however, the generalist must rely on intelligence applied to memory, on the useful knowledge he carries around with him. I will draft the following answers, but it is safe to say that no two generalists will have exactly the same wording, and in one or two cases there might be considerable difference of opinion.

The reference books I have within easy reach of my desk are these:

Latest edition of *Encyclopaedia Britannica*, twenty-four volumes, plus Annuals
Encyclopaedia of the Social Sciences, eight volumes
Columbia–Viking Desk Encyclopedia, one volume
Hammond's World Atlas
World Almanac, annual
Information Please Almanac, annual
Shorter Oxford Dictionary, two volumes
Webster's New World Dictionary, one volume
Latin, German, French and Spanish dictionaries
Who's Who in America
Bartlett's Familiar Quotations
Roget's Thesaurus

Modern English Usage, Fowler

A *Dictionary of Contemporary American Usage*, Evans

SUGGESTED ANSWERS TO THE 25 QUESTIONS

1. From gas and dust clouds.

2. Perhaps 4.5 billion years.

3. Copernicus removed the earth, and with it man, from the center of the universe.

4. Individuals who best adjust to the environment breed, and gradually change the species. Houseflies resistant to DDT breed, and develop a strain beyond the reach of DDT.

5. Man makes artificial adjustments to the environment, via houses, clothing, oil burners, etc.

6. None.

7. What are his frustrations?

8. Language.

9. Weightlessness, re-entry, radiation, meteors.

10. Science is an orderly growth, and at some point new knowledge is needed if growth is to continue. Various scientists become acutely aware of this need and strive to fill it, often quite independently of one another.

11. War.

12. A storable food, normally grain.

13. Members of a species best equipped to meet a changing environment survive. Strength and ruthlessness may have little to do with it, as in the case of houseflies and DDT.

14. Democracy cannot function without a large, educated middle class, a class which some republics lack.

15. The shift of power from the owners of many large corporations to a self-perpetuating group of managers. Marx predicted that the power of owners would increase.

16. No. I deduce that while man has an inborn tendency to violence, he has none for organized warfare.

17. No. I deduce that a brain which can master the Eskimo language can master a cyclotron.

18. Easing of credit, reduction of taxes, public works.

19. No. Russia does not rely on consumer spending for equilibrium, but controls the output of consumer goods.

20. By restricting the production of consumer goods.

21. No, not with modern money.

22. Newtonian physics postulated certain absolutes—absolute Time, absolute Space, etc. Modern science has replaced absolutes with probabilities, processes, relativity and the uncertainty principle.

23. The culture concept; perception theory; sampling theory.

24. Keeping an open mind, gathering the facts, checking conclusions by controlled experiments.

25. Science demands a degree of honesty, and an ability to say "I am wrong," not often found in other occupations.

ANSWERS TO QUESTIONS IN GALLUP'S
  CULTURAL OLYMPICS (cited in Chapter 1, page 2)

Dante

Islam

Socrates

That population tends to outrun food supply

Russian behavioral scientist

The biological unit transmitting inheritance

1912

The amount of work delivered by a heat engine depends on temperature difference

Das Kapital

Free competition, no interference with the market

Freud

Islam, Buddhism, Confucianism

Stone support for a wall, often for cathedral walls

Descartes

Opera house in Milan

Sibelius

A Reading List for Generalists

The list of books which follows is a mere sample, and perforce omits many valuable and absorbing works. Not only that but the books suggested point to many others, and the generalist, if he has the curiosity and enthusiasm that go with his role, will continue to explore far beyond these few titles. Where there is a choice of equally good books, the more recent one is listed. The classification is rough, as some of the subjects overlap and shade into each other. The main sources of the present book are included, except where they are too technical.

BACKGROUND READING

WHITE, LYNN, JR., editor: *Frontiers of Knowledge in the Study of Man.* Harper, 1956.

The President of Mills College edits a symposium where specialists discuss such specialties as culture (Clyde Kluckhohn), archeology (Gordon R. Willey), political science (Peter Odegard) and history (Mr. White himself). Most of the essays are excellent.

FLANAGAN, DENNIS and others, editors: *The Scientific American Reader.* Simon and Schuster, 1953.

Specialists, mostly in the natural sciences, report late technical findings clearly and with authority. The monthly *Scientific American* itself, skillfully edited for both layman and specialist, covers many fields in their rapid development, reporting both social and natural science.

PRYCE-JONES, ALAN, editor: *The New Outline of Modern Knowledge.* Simon and Schuster, 1956.

Twenty-six experts supposedly bring "the ordinary intelligent man" up to date on progress in their fields since 1930. The fields range from analytical philosophy and metaphysical speculation, through eight branches of science, seven of art, and six of politics and economics, to law; and the treatment sometimes becomes rather complex.

CHILDE, V. G.: *Society and Knowledge*. World Perspectives Series, Vol. 6. Harper, 1956.

Emphasizing communication and culture patterns, this London archeologist leaves his specialty to consider knowledge in general as a practical tool.

FRANKEL, CHARLES: *The Case for Modern Man*. Harper, 1956.

A professor of philosophy at Columbia looks at man today in the light of his history and argues that we can make a better world by using our intelligence.

WELLS, H. G.: *The Fate of Man*. Longmans, Green, 1939.

Few writers have viewed the human race with a longer perspective; few have made more stimulating prophecies.

EVANS, BERGEN: *The Natural History of Nonsense*. Knopf, 1946.

Some prize exhibits in anti-knowledge.

MACKAY, CHARLES: *Extraordinary Popular Delusions and the Madness of Crowds*. L. P. Page, 1841, 1852. Farrar Straus and Cudahy, 1932.

More anti-knowledge; a favorite book of Bernard M. Baruch.

ASTROPHYSICS, GEOLOGY, THE EARTH

HOYLE, FRED: *The Nature of the Universe*. Harper, 1950.

Julian Huxley called this "a brilliant book which manages to give in brief compass an unforgettable picture of the cosmos and its development as seen by modern astronomy."

THIEL, RUDOLF: *And There Was Light; the Discovery of the Universe*. Knopf, 1957.

Long and comprehensive history of ancient astronomy and modern astrophysics, excellently illustrated, clearly written and translated from the German.

CLASON, CLYDE B.: *Exploring the Distant Stars*. Putnam, 1958.

An American covers much of the same ground as Thiel.

WYLER, ROSE, and AMES, GERALD: *The Golden Book of Astronomy*. Simon and Schuster, 1955.

A journalistic treatment, intended for young people, mostly about the earth and solar system, and ending with a discussion of space exploration. Copious sketches and diagrams are helpful in spite of rather lurid colors.

BERNHARD, HUBERT J., and others, editors: *Handbook of the Heavens*. Whittlesey House, McGraw Hill, 1935.

Also for young people but more technical than the *Golden Book*, this work was produced by a collaboration between the Junior Astronomy Clubs, the Hayden Planetarium in New York, and astronomers at several observatories.

MARSHACK, ALEXANDER: *The World in Space; the Story of the International Geophysical Year*. Thomas Nelson & Sons, 1958.

Background and projects of the Year, with sections on land, ocean, air, magnetism, ionosphere, sun, etc. Charts, drawings, photographs.

MOORE, RUTH: *The Earth We Live On*. Knopf, 1956.

A journalist's careful chronological account of geological discovery.

LIFE AND EVOLUTION

EISELY, LOREN: *The Immense Journey*. Random House, 1957.

In these entertaining essays a specialist in human paleontology describes some adventures in his field work, and reflects on crucial stages in evolution.

KRUTCH, JOSEPH WOOD: *The Great Chain of Life*. Houghton Mifflin, 1956.

A nontechnical discussion of evolution, with conclusions about individualism, written with the author's well-known charm. No index nor bibliography.

HUXLEY, JULIAN: *Evolution in Action*. Harper, 1953.

A "telescopic book" by a biologist, emphasizing philosophic aspects.

BECK, WILLIAM S.: *Modern Science and the Nature of Life*. Harcourt, 1957.

Readable outline of the history of biology, ending with some great unanswered questions in genetics.

SCHEINFELD, AMRAM: *The New You and Heredity*. Lippincott, 1950.

Human genetics, a comprehensive and careful account.

ARCHEOLOGY AND PRE-HISTORY

BIBBY, GEOFFREY: *Testimony of the Spade*. Knopf. 1956.

A British archeologist who lives in Denmark traces consecutively what is known of the earliest European migrations and settlements, with graphic accounts of the hard work and brilliant deduction that revealed the knowledge.

WENDT, HERBERT: *In Search of Adam*. Houghton Mifflin, 1956.

One of the numerous recent translations of German books on

popular science, this book recounts the work of various explorers and scientists who contributed to our knowledge of proto-man and ancient man. Parallels Bibby's book in part, and is harder going.

MONTAGU, M. F. ASHLEY: *Man, His First Million Years*. World Publishing Co., 1957.

An anthropologist and popular writer collects evidence from various sources about the age, origin and characteristics of man. He covers a wide span, and concentrates on conclusions rather than the people who drew them.

HOWELLS, WILLIAM: *Mankind So Far*. Doubleday, 1944.

Lively and readable, endorsed by the American Museum of Natural History, this book necessarily omits later discoveries, including one that would have saved the author much anxiety, the great Piltdown hoax.

COON, CARLETON S.: *The Seven Caves*. Knopf, 1957.

The author's own excavations at sites from North Africa to Afghanistan, seeking Neanderthal and other early remains. Entertaining stories of native workmen.

ANCIENT FARMS AND CITIES

CHILDE, V. G.: *Man Makes Himself*. Mentor Books, 1951.

A great British archeologist analyzes "progress through early stages of culture and knowledge," describing the neolithic revolution and the urban revolution in the valleys of the Nile, the Indus, and the twin rivers of the Mid East.

COON, CARLETON S.: *The Story of Man; from the First Human to Primitive Culture and Beyond*. Knopf, 1954.

Admitting frankly the gaps in current knowledge, Coon leans to West-Central Asia as the birthplace of Homo sapiens. He thinks there may have been a number of types of pre-human primates on different continents before the Ice Ages.

FRANKFORT, HENRI: *The Birth of Civilization in the Near East*. Doubleday, Anchor Books, 1956.

Absorbing account of the earliest cities in Mesopotamia and Egypt, with attention to their problems of administration and government, and possible diffusion between Egypt and Mesopotamia.

KELLER, WERNER: *The Bible as History*. Morrow, 1957.

Evidence about the actual movements of the ancient Hebrews, their migrations and early cities, ties in with Frankfort's book and tends to support the biblical accounts. Translated from the German.

WALLACE, HENRY A. and BROWN, WILLIAM L.: *Corn and Its Early Fathers.* Michigan State University Press, 1956.

Research into the history and pre-history of corn, which has been bred continuously for many thousands of years (otherwise it would have died out), longer the authors think than any other grain.

MORLEY, SYLVANUS GRISWOLD: *The Ancient Maya.* Stanford University Press, 1946.

The complex and sophisticated civilization of the Maya, reconstructed by an archeologist who spent most of his life studying what remains of that civilization.

BLOM, FRANZ: *The Conquest of Yucatan.* Houghton Mifflin, 1936.

A shorter book, describing the end of the Maya civilization, by another archeologist, who is still at work in Mexico.

HISTORY, CULTURAL CHANGE

MULLER, HERBERT J.: *The Uses of the Past; Profiles of Former Societies.* Oxford University Press, 1952.

Viewing the past in a mood of tragic irony, the author offers new insights into both familiar and unfamiliar periods.

WELLS, H. G.: *The Outline of History.* Garden City Publishing Co., revised 1931.

Again, the author's long perspective, historic sense and gift for prophecy make this a valuable work for the generalist. Useful too for quick reference and time comparisons.

MILLER, WILLIAM: *A History of the United States.* George Braziller, 1958.

From the Spanish explorers to the foreign policy of Secretary Dulles, this sound and readable short history is characterized by a specialist as "what a mature adult would like to read and think about."

OGBURN, WILLIAM F.: *Social Change, with Respect to Culture and Original Nature.* Viking, revised 1950.

The first statement, largely theoretic, of the accelerating spiral of technology.

SPICER, EDWARD H., editor: *Human Problems in Technological Change.* Russell Sage Foundation, 1952.

Fourteen contributors describe the introduction of new tools and methods in primitive societies from Peru to Alaska to the Micronesian Islands.

USHER, ABBOTT PAYSON: *A History of Mechanical Inventions.* McGraw-Hill, 1929.

A scholar and economist at Harvard shows, along with much technical detail, the interrelation of technologic and economic progress, and describes the beginnings of mechanical invention in ancient history.

BURLINGAME, ROGER: *March of the Iron Men.* Scribner, 1938.

First of three scholarly volumes on invention and technical progress in the United States.

BROWN, HARRISON, and others: *The Next Hundred Years; Man's Natural and Technological Resources.* Viking, 1957.

What technology is doing to the earth and to life. Scientists extrapolate its progress, with gloomy predictions.

CULTURE AND BEHAVIOR

KLUCKHOHN, CLYDE: *Mirror for Man; the Relation of Anthropology to Modern Life.* Whittlesey House, McGraw-Hill, 1949.

A brief, clear interpretation for the layman, with conclusions as well as illustrative cases.

GILLIN, JOHN: *The Ways of Men; An Introduction to Anthropology.* Appleton-Century, 1948.

This thorough but not over-technical exposition, intended as a textbook, begins with pre-human primates, emphasizes psychological aspects, and inquires what goals a desirable culture should steer for.

MEAD, MARGARET: *Sex and Temperament in Three Primitive Societies.* Morrow, 1935.

Contrasts the folkways of neighboring tribes in New Guinea. Like all Dr. Mead's books, it communicates clearly and attractively.

BENEDICT, RUTH: *Patterns of Culture.* Houghton Mifflin, 1934.

This readable and popular classic, available also in paperback edition, traces the dramatic effects of their differing belief systems on the life of two tribes of American Indians and one in New Guinea.

OGBURN, WILLIAM F., and NIMKOFF, M. F.: *Sociology.* Houghton Mifflin, revised 1958.

Excellent introductory college textbook, long and thorough, interpreting society in the light of the culture concept.

DOLLARD, JOHN, and others: *Frustration and Aggression.* Yale University Press, 1939.

Specialists in different social sciences collaborated to produce this scrupulously detailed book. They apply their theory to personal and political life, primitive peoples, international relations.

ALLPORT, GORDON W.: *The Nature of Prejudice.* Beacon Press–Addison Wesley, 1954.

With cases and examples from all over the world, this long and definitive book by a Harvard psychologist is probably the first to analyze prejudice in a systematic way, and attack the problem from both practical and theoretic points of view.

LANGUAGE AND COMMUNICATION

JOHNSON, WENDELL: *People in Quandaries; The Semantics of Personal Adjustment*. Harper, 1946.

Though this book is long and perhaps over-psychiatric, it embodies the author's experience in guidance and counseling, as well as in teaching speech, and suggests many applications.

LEE, IRVING and LAURA: *Handling Barriers in Communication; Lecture-Discussions and Conferee's Handbook*. Harper, 1957.

A course, based on the case method, originally given to Bell Telephone supervisors. Not only offers semantically sound material, but acquaints the reader with the work of a great lecturer and teacher.

HAYAKAWA, S. I.: *Language in Thought and Action*. Harcourt, 1949.

Clear presentation of the general theory of semantics by the editor of the specialized quarterly *ETC*.

HAYAKAWA, S. I., editor: *Language, Meaning and Maturity*. Harper, 1954.

Selected essays from a decade of *ETC*. include contributions by Irving Lee, Carl Rogers, Alfred Korzybski, Anatol Rapaport, Wendell Johnson, Charles Morris.

SAPIR, EDWARD: *Culture, Language and Personality*. University of Calif. Press, 1956.

Nine selected essays, edited by David Mandelbaum, seventeen years after the author's untimely death. Sapir, who was born in Germany, educated in the United States, and taught at four universities, received many academic honors for his original research.

WHORF, BENJAMIN LEE: *Language, Thought and Reality*. Massachusetts Institute of Technology Press, 1956.

A friend of Sapir's explains the theory that language shapes our thoughts—a theory which its author did not live long enough to prove. Examples from the Hopi and other Indian languages.

HOGBEN, LANCELOT: *From Cave Painting to Comic Strip; A Kaleidoscope of Human Communication*. Chanticleer Press, 1949.

This lively book, profusely illustrated, disguises the scholarship it shares with an earlier work by Hogben in collaboration with F. Bodmer, *The Loom of Language*.

PEI, MARIO: *One Language for the World, and How to Achieve It.* Devin-Adair, 1958.

Without advocating any particular language for world use, the author, a well-known professor and authority on linguistics, outlines the pressing need for such a world language, reviews many earlier proposals (dating from the Tower of Babel) and offers a solution for this urgent problem.

ECONOMICS

SOULE, GEORGE: *Ideas of the Great Economists.* Viking, 1952.

Good summary of the classicists' theories.

BERLE, ADOLF A., JR.: *The Twentieth Century Capitalist Revolution.* Harcourt, 1954.

Analysis of capitalism in the present day, with the corporation as the focus of attention.

GALBRAITH, J. K.: *The Affluent Society.* Houghton Mifflin, 1958.

A fresh and penetrating analysis of the American economy, where poverty has been abolished for the majority, but at a price. Suggestions for restoring balance.

HERSKOVITS, MELVILLE J.: *The Economic Life of Primitive Peoples.* Knopf, 1940.

Detailed account by a distinguished anthropologist of economic behavior in modern primitive societies, where women usually do the farm and garden labor, and men hunt and trade.

POLITICS

ROPER, ELMO: *You and Your Leaders.* Morrow, 1958.

Nine current or recent political figures in the United States, described and analyzed in the light of opinion polls.

APPLEBY, PAUL H.: *Big Democracy.* Knopf, 1945.

Wise discussion by a long-time civil servant of various problems of administration and the philosophy of government.

BEARD, CHARLES A.: *The Republic; Conversation on Fundamentals.* Viking, 1943.

Cast in the form of a Socratic dialogue, this book by the late specialist in American history and the problems of government examines both with keen insight.

STEVENSON, ADLAI: *Call to Greatness.* Harper, 1954.

After touring 30 countries and capitals from Seoul to Berlin and interviewing their leaders, the Democratic candidate for President in 1952 delivered these lectures at Harvard on problems confronting the United States and the "free world."

BUCHANAN, WILLIAM, and CANTRIL, HADLEY: *How Nations See Each Other; A Study in Public Opinion.* University of Illinois Press, 1953. International polls, taken under the auspices of UNESCO.

SHAFER, BOYD C.: *Nationalism, Myth and Reality.* Harcourt, 1955.

Cogent and scholarly inquiry by a historian into the meaning and origin of "the chief problem of our time."

DE HEGEDUS, ADAM: *Patriotism or Peace?* Scribner, 1947.

A shorter book than Shafer's, with less documentation, in which nationalism is represented as a historical accident.

FOSDICK, RAYMOND B.: *Within Our Power; Perspective for a Time of Peril.* Longmans, Green, 1952.

A great generalist discusses prospects for a unified world—hopefully.

SCIENCE AND THE SCIENTIFIC ATTITUDE

BRONOWSKI, J.: *The Common Sense of Science.* Harvard University Press, 1953.

A British mathematician (and student of poetry as well) attempts to clarify science for the layman. He is more successful with historic illustrations and anecdotes than with abstract conclusions about what "science is." His later book, *Science and Human Values,* is still more abstract, but makes some good points.

TAYLOR, F. SHERWOOD: *The World of Science.* Reynal & Hitchcock, 1937.

In spite—or perhaps because—of being somewhat out-of-date, this comprehensive British work supplies useful background and reference material under six headings: The States of Matter, Power, Waves, Chemistry, The Earth and Heavens, and Life.

HOGBEN, LANCELOT: *Science for the Citizen; A Self-Educator Based on the Social Background of Scientific Discovery.* Knopf, 1938.

Even longer than Taylor's work, perhaps more readable because of a narrative framework and thread of history.

PEARSON, KARL: *The Grammar of Science.* London, Walter Scott, 1892.

A classic that retains its interest and general validity.

HECHT, SELIG: *Explaining the Atom.* Viking, 1947.

Remains the clearest presentation to my knowledge of this difficult subject. For later corrections in detail, see *Scientific American Reader*, listed above, or the monthly *Scientific American*.

FRANK, LAWRENCE K.: *Nature and Human Nature; Man's New Image of Himself.* Rutgers University Press, 1951.

A noted psychologist and educator points out that new knowledge of man and his environment calls for new ways of thinking about the world and ourselves.

Other works on scientific subjects have been mentioned in the earlier, more specific sections of this list. Since the present author has written some books in several of the above fields, and everything he writes is addressed to generalists, a few of his own titles are appended.

His *Proper Study of Mankind* gives a short explanation of social anthropology and the culture concept; *Mexico* offers some sidelights and illustrations of the same subject. *Power of Words* and *The Tyranny of Words* deal with semantics, language and communication. Economics is treated in *The Economy of Abundance, Where's the Money Coming From?* and a number of others; aspects of behavior—especially group behavior—in *Roads to Agreement* and *Men at Work*, as well as in the *Proper Study. Democracy under Pressure* deals with pressure groups in politics, *Rich Land, Poor Land* with conservation of resources and respectful treatment of the earth.

INDEX

273